LEARN MORE TO

Hobbyists and Students

ELECTRONICS GUIDES

Radiomans Guide
Television Repair Manual

ENGINEERS' GUIDES

Power Plant Engineers Guide
Questions & Answers for Engineers and Firemans Examinations

HEATING GUIDES

Oil Burner Guide
Questions & Answers for Engineers and Firemans Examinations
House Heating Guide

MACHINISTS' GUIDES

Welders Guide
New Mechanical Dictionary
Mathematics & Calculations for Mechanics
Machinists & Tool Makers Handy Book

MATHEMATICS GUIDES

Mathematics & Calculations for Mechanics
Electrical Power Calculations

MECHANICS' GUIDES

Oil Burner Guide
Refrigeration & Air Conditioning Guide
Auto Mechanics Guide
Home Appliance Service Guide
Mathematics & Calculations for Mechanics
Millwrights & Mechanics Guide
New Mechanical Dictionary

PAINTING AND DECORATING

Painting & Decorating Manual

PHOTOGRAPHY

Guide to Creative Photography

PLUMBING

Plumbers & Steamfitters Guides (4 vols.)

PUMPS

Pumps—Hydraulics—Air Compressors

REFRIGERATION AND AIR CONDITIONING

Refrigeration & Air Conditioning Guide

SCIENCE GUIDES

Encyclopedia of Space Science
Practical Chemistry for Everyone

SHEET METAL GUIDES

Sheet Metal Pattern Layouts
Sheet Metal Workers Handy Book

WELDING

Welders Guide

ENDORSED BY EXPERIENCE

"Have never had the pleasure of reading books such as yours, that explain most difficult problems so easily and look so nice on a shelf."

"Have many Audel books and they are worth their weight in gold to me."

"Am pleased with the books: Don't think I could find another set that can match these in value anywhere."

"Since receiving my Guides I have received increased responsibility and income. The books give one confidence to tackle the problems that arise, with confidence."

"Well pleased. Very comprehensible and a mighty handy reference book."

"A great help. Your liberal terms make it possible for anyone to obtain a practical education."

Cat. No. AUD-97

PRACTICAL GUIDE TO SERVICING ELECTRONIC ORGANS

by Carl R. Pittman & Eugene J. Oliver

THEODORE AUDEL & CO.

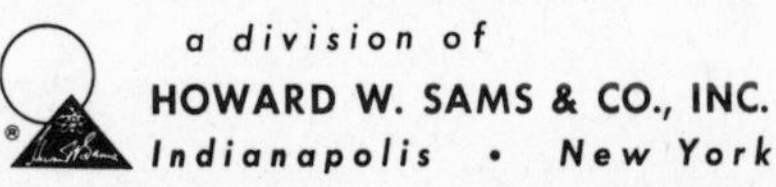
a division of
HOWARD W. SAMS & CO., INC.
Indianapolis • New York

FIRST EDITION

FIRST PRINTING — MAY, 1965

PRACTICAL GUIDE TO SERVICING ELECTRONIC ORGANS

Library of Congress Catalog Card Number: 65-19028

Foreword

Electronic organs have opened a new servicing field which offers excellent opportunities to the enterprising service technician.

Before he can troubleshoot and repair electronic organs efficiently, however, a technician must have an understanding of the basic theories involved in the operation of electronic organs, and be familiar with the circuitry employed in the various models now available.

The principal circuits involved in this type of equipment (oscillators, switches, waveshaping networks, and audio amplifiers) are already familiar to most service technicians. The purpose of this book, then, is to show how these circuits work, individually and in combination, to produce the variety of organ tones and sound effects.

With a thorough understanding and proper application of this knowledge, the competent service technician should have little or no difficulty in making adjustments or repairs on modern electronic organs.

Our sincere gratitude to the following manufacturers whose technical and illustrative contributions helped make this book possible:

Allen Organ Company, Baldwin Piano Company, Conn Organ Corp., Hammond Organ Company, Kinsman Manufacturing Company Inc., Lowrey Organ Company, Magnavox Company, Thomas Organ Company, The Wurlitzer Company, and Electro-Music Company.

CARL R. PITTMAN & EUGENE J. OLIVER

Contents

CHAPTER 1

INTRODUCTION 7

Musical Terms—Basic Organ Circuits

CHAPTER 2

TONE GENERATORS 21

Mechanical Tone Generators—Electronic Tone Generators

CHAPTER 3

PEDAL GENATORS AND PEDAL SUSTAIN 49

Conn — Lowrey — Wurlitzer — Magnavox — Thomas — Hammond — Allen — Kinsman

CHAPTER 4

VIBRATO AND TREMOLO 77

Phase-Shift Oscillator — Wurlitzer — Thomas — Lowrey — Conn — Baldwin — Magnavox — Hammond — Allen — Kinsman

CHAPTER 5

KEYSWITCHES 111

Hammond — Conn — Wurlitzer — Magnavox — Baldwin — Thomas

CHAPTER 6

PERCUSSION 129

Hammond—Kinsman—Thomas—Baldwin—Allen

CHAPTER 7

SUSTAIN 157

Wurlitzer — Lowrey — Kinsman — Conn — Magnavox — Allen

CHAPTER 8

VOICING 177

Wurlitzer — Hammond — Allen — Kinsman — Thomas — Lowrey — Pedal Voicing Circuits — Outphase Voices

CHAPTER 9

AMPLIFIERS AND POWER SUPPLIES 195

Magnavox — Conn Generator Regulator — Kinsman — Expression Controls

CHAPTER 10

TUNING AND ADJUSTMENT PROCEDURES 207

General Organ Checkout Procedure — Tuning

CHAPTER 11

ACCESSORIES 221

Leslie Speaker Units — Allen Speaker Units

GLOSSARY 235

INDEX 241

CHAPTER 1

Introduction

The growing popularity of the electronic organ has opened a new avenue of service for the technician. Moreover, the demand for qualified technicians to service this type of equipment increases with every new model that goes on the market. The servicing potential will be obvious to the forward-looking technician, and he will undoubtedly have a desire to learn all he possibly can about this relatively new aspect of electronic servicing.

All electronic organs are basically the same, however, there is a wide variation in circuit design and application among the different makes and models. While the end result is usually quite similar, the method of achieving it may vary considerably from one organ to another.

As with any other apparatus, the technician should devise a troubleshooting pattern that will enable him to restore an electronic organ's performance with the least amount of time and effort. A careful analysis of the trouble symptoms will be of significant value in isolating the defective circuit and making the necessary repairs as quickly and efficiently as possible. Although at first glance the inside of an electronic organ may appear rather complex, it is actually comprised of numerous electronic circuits, generally of conventional design and already familiar to most service technicians.

MUSICAL TERMS

Many of the terms encountered in connection with the organ will probably be new to you. Those fortunate enough to have a musical background will grasp these new terms quite readily; however, lack of any previous musical training will be of no handicap to the competent technician.

The purpose of every electronic organ is to produce a tone, which is a combination of pitch and timbre. *Pitch* is most accurately described as the discrimination of one audio frequency from another. Frequency, an exact number of cycles based on the note of the musical scale, is the basis for establishing pitch. *Timbre,* on the other hand, is the characteristic by which one musical instrument can be distinguished from another instrument playing the same note. Timbre depends on the overtones or harmonics produced by an instrument. The duration and volume of the tone also influences the tonal quality.

Before the pitch of any audio tone can be determined, there first must be a reference point. Thus, the degree to which a particular note is off pitch is relative to the correct pitch, or frequency, of that note.

One method of detecting pitch is to sound two tones in close succession. The pitch may be determined by detecting the *beating* of the two tones, or the difference in their frequency. If one of the tones remains at the reference frequency as the other tone is brought closer to it, a point will occur where no difference in pitch is discernible. This point is the *limit of pitch discrimination,* and is defined as the minimum difference in pitch an individual can detect. As in all sound characteristics, however, the detection or discrimination of pitch will vary from one person to another. Moreover, the human ear cannot detect exact pitch; only with precise instruments such as the *Strobotuner* (discussed in a later chapter) can this be done. With practice, however, the ear can be trained to determine the correct pitch of a musical note with surprising accuracy.

Frequency changes are more easily detected at the high audio frequencies. Pitch may also vary directly with the volume (amplitude) of the sound by as much as one full note.

Two more musical terms common to all organs are *tremolo* and *vibrato*. Tremolo is the pulsating change in intensity; vibrato is a constant variation of pitch accompanied by a slight pulsation in loudness and timbre. Tremolo may be considered a form of amplitude modulation, whereas vibrato is primarily a frequency modulation.

Tablet, or tab, is the name given to the device for selecting a particular function of the organ. In pipe-organ terminology the the equivalent controls are called *stops* because their purpose is to open or close the pipes. Even in some electronic organs, the tabs are referred to as stops.

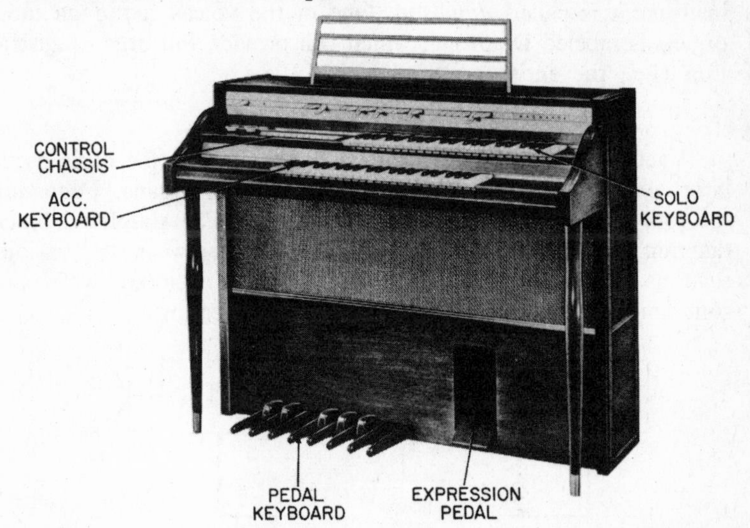

Courtesy Magnavox Company.

Fig. 1-1. Magnavox Model A-10 organ.

Manual describes the keyboard of the organ. The manual may consist of two or more keyboards called *accompaniment* and *solo,* or *great* and *swell* (the name varies according to manufacturer). The keyboard operated with the feet is called the *pedalboard,* and sometimes the *clavier*. Fig. 1-1 shows the control and keyboard arrangement used with the Magnavox Model A-10 electronic organ.

Sustain and *voices* are two more common terms associated with the organ. Sustain is the term relating to the continued sounding of a note after the key has been released; and voices or voicing, the simulation of the sound of a particular instrument by the organ. Voicing circuits are sometimes referred to as formant circuits since they establish the condition for the timbre quality of all tones sounded from the instrument. The entire range of the instrument is called *diapason*. One of the voices found on most organs is labeled Diapason, which will provide full organ registration (i.e., the entire range).

BASIC ORGAN CIRCUITS

Vacuum tubes and transistors are employed as the basic oscillator, or tone-generating device, in electronic organs. Following the tone generator are the formant circuits. The simplified block diagram in Fig. 1-2 shows the relationship between the various sections. The tone generators are basic oscillator circuits which are sometimes modified to meet the specific application.

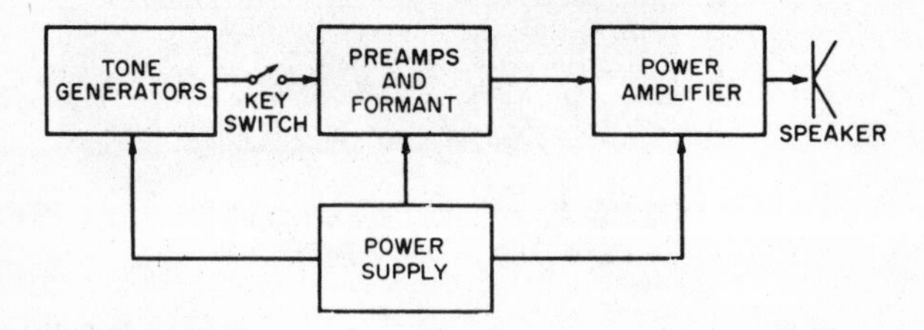

Fig. 1-2. Simplified block diagram of an electronic organ.

For a thorough understanding of tone generators and the part they play in the make-up of the organ, it might be well to review a few basic oscillator circuits.

To produce the tones, self-starting, continuous oscillations are necessary for proper stability and dependability. These oscillations are obtained by coupling some of the energy from the plate circuit of the oscillator either inductively or electrostatically to the grid circuit. This signal energy must be of sufficient amplitude and have the proper phase relationship before these oscillations will occur, however.

Probably the most common oscillator in use today is the Hartley, illustrated in Fig. 1-3. One definite advantage is the simplicity of its basic circuitry; the number of components depends on its application and on the amount of loading to be encountered.

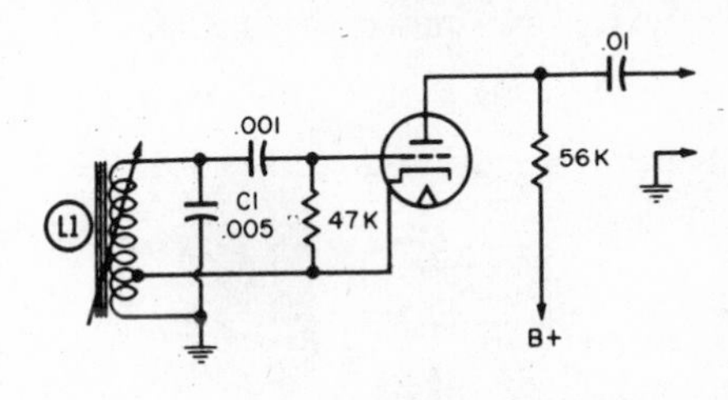

(A) Vacuum-tube version.

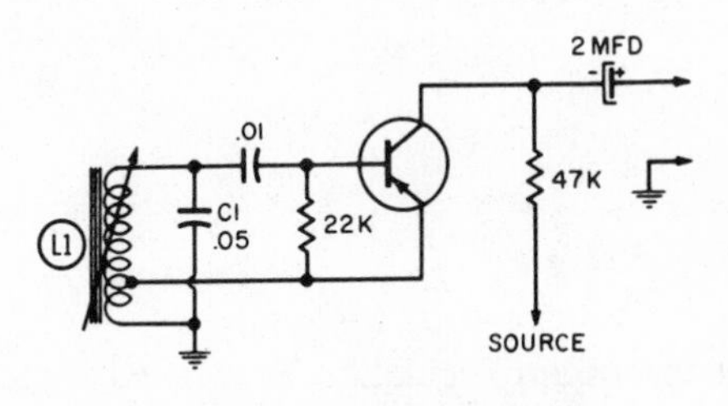

(B) Transistor version.

Fig. 1-3. Typical Hartley oscillator.

Another feature of the Hartley oscillator is its excellent frequency stability, an important factor at the frequencies which must be covered in the electronic organ. Because of the low frequencies at which the oscillator in the organ must function, the tank circuit and its associated components may be quite large, compared to the local oscillator in a radio receiver.

The inductance of this circuit is generally a tapped iron core autotransformer (L1), and usually is variable by changing the spacing of the air gap in the core. The output frequency of this oscillator will depend on the values of L1 and C1.

Another oscillator circuit which deserves mention is the Colpitts, illustrated in Fig. 1-4. This circuit is easily distinguished by the capacitive divider (C1 and C2) across the tank circuit. Its self-stabilizing characteristic makes the Colpitts oscillator extremely desirable for use under varying loads.

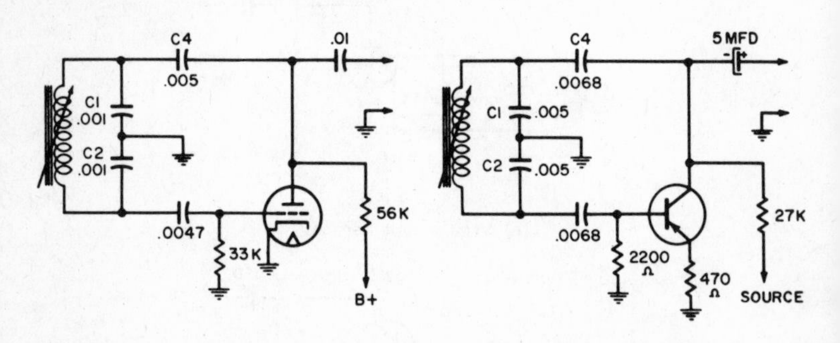

(A) Vacuum-tube version.

(B) Transistor version.

Fig. 1-4. Typical Colpitts oscillator.

Feedback to sustain oscillation is coupled directly to the top of the tank circuit via C4. This provides a highly reliable means of obtaining the proper phase relationship, as well as the proper amplitude to provide a self-sustaining condition.

The basic mutivibrator circuit is illustrated in Fig. 1-5. Primarily, it is nothing more than two amplifier circuits with the output of one coupled to the input of the other, and vice versa.

The frequency of oscillation is determined by the R-C time constants of the grid circuits. The plate load resistor that is used will have little or no effect on the operating frequency. As a

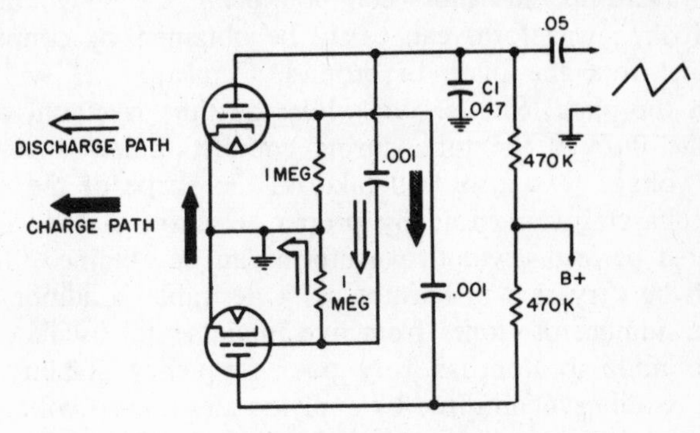

(A) Vacuum-tube version.

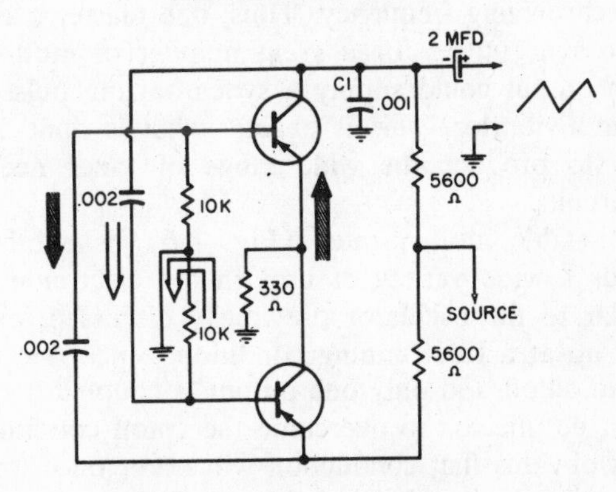

(B) Transistor version.

Fig. 1-5. Typical multivibrator circuits.

matter of fact, in special organ circuits an inductance may be substituted for the plate load. The output waveform will then approach a sine wave because of the ringing effect the inductance has on the multivibrator output.

The "raw" output of the multivibrator may consist of numerous waveforms, the most common being the sawtooth shown here. Such a waveform can easily be obtained by connecting a capacitor from the plate to ground. Capacitor C1 will charge through the plate load resistor while the tube is cutoff, and will discharge through the tube during conduction. As a result, the output voltage waveform will take on the shape of the charging and discharging capacitor. By proper selection of the capacitor, an almost perfect sawtooth waveform can be obtained. The output will be very rich in harmonics, a desirable condition for deriving a number of tones from one fundamental oscillator.

The multivibrator has very poor frequency stability, but it may be readily synchronized by applying an external voltage pulse. It may actually be synchronized to run at a division or multiple of the synchronizing frequency. Thus, one master oscillator could supply the sync pulses for a great number of multivibrators. In turn, each output could supply a synchronizing pulse to the succeeding multivibrator. This is exactly what is done in a number of organs to produce the wide range of tones needed for the voicing circuits.

The bi-stable multivibrator (Fig. 1-6), is another oscillator which finds a wide variety of uses in the electronic organ. It is very similar to the oscillator previously discussed, except that it is not set up at a free-running condition. Since one of the tubes is biased to cutoff and only one output is coupled back, a voltage pulse must be injected to overcome the cutoff condition. If this is done, it is obvious that conduction will occur once for each pulse applied to the tube that is normally cutoff.

The output waveform may take on many shapes. One of the most common is the square wave. It is obtained by taking the

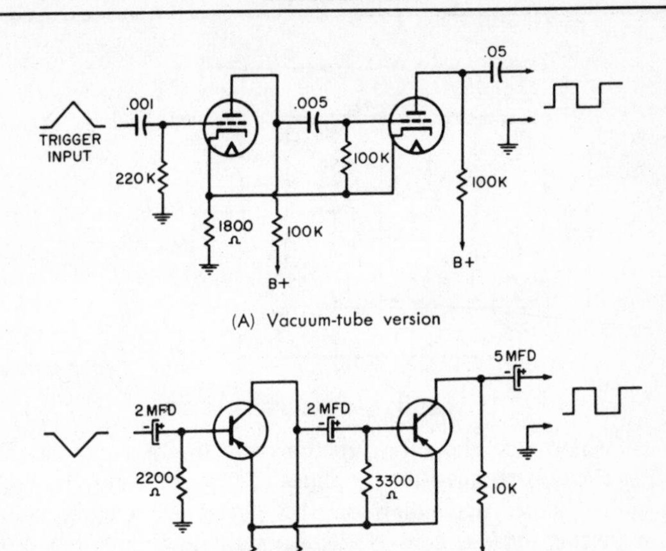

(A) Vacuum-tube version

(B) Transistor version.

Fig. 1-6. Typical Eccles-Jordan circuit.

tube from which the output is removed and operating it at saturation so that the signal is clipped. Since the square wave produces an infinite number of harmonics, a variety of tones may be derived by filtering out the unwanted harmonics. In this manner, a wide range of frequencies is available for the organ voicing. The square wave also provides an excellent pulse to sync another multivibrator or flip-flop circuit for frequency division.

The electron-coupled multivibrator illustrated in Fig. 1-7, operates exactly like a conventional multivibrator. The only difference is in the way the load is coupled to the oscillator. Two pentodes are employed, but their screen grids are connected in

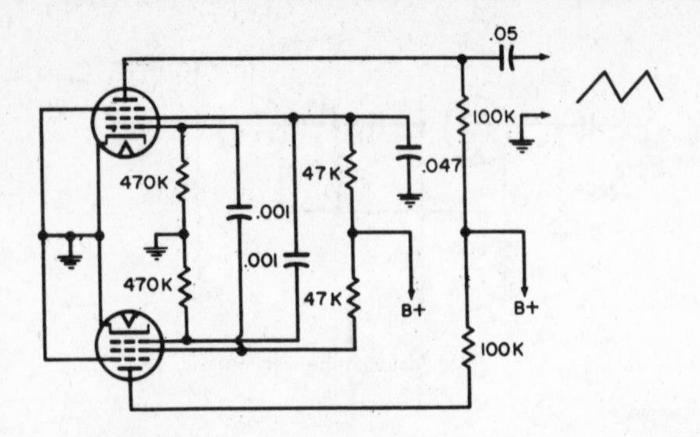

Fig. 1-7. Typical electron-coupled multivibrator.

such a fashion that the tube functions much like a triode. The signal is electron coupled to the plates. The output may be taken from either plate, depending on the phase desired. A unique feature of this arrangement is the isolation maintained between the oscillator and its associated load. This circuit operates very well in the vibrato or tremolo generator, where a signal must be provided to a number of circuits.

Still another circuit with which you should be familiar is the phase-shift oscillator, illustrated in Fig. 1-8. This circuit differs slightly from the oscillators to which most service technicians are accustomed, but its operation is very simple to understand.

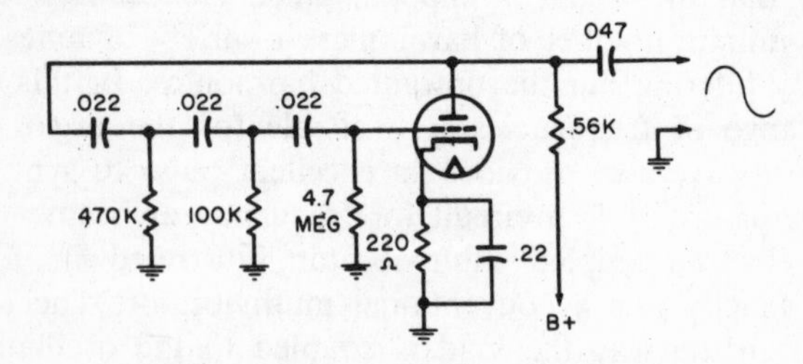

Fig. 1-8. Typical phase-shift oscillator.

Notice that three R-C networks are series-parallel connected from the grid back to the plate. The values of these R-C networks are chosen so that the signal fed to the grid from the plate is approximately 180° out of phase. When this type of oscillator is adjusted to the point where oscillations are barely maintained, good frequency stability as well as sine-wave output may be realized.

The phase-shift oscillator is especially useful in providing a low-frequency signal to those circuits where stability is required, such as the vibrato or tremolo generator.

The oscillators, or tone generators, are only the first step toward obtaining music from the organ. Following the oscillators are the voicing circuits.

Voicing Circuits

Basically, the voicing circuits are nothing more than simple waveshaping networks into which the signals from the tone generators are fed. These networks are necessary since the timbre quality of any sound is dependent on the harmonic content of the sound. Thus, in order for the electronic organ to simulate instruments, the waveform must be given the required shape before it enters the final audio amplifier.

The waveshaping networks may then be classed as simple filter networks. Since the shape of an electrical waveform depends on its harmonic content, the filter network must be designed to pass the desired harmonics of the waveform. Thus the shape of the waveform will be altered to coincide with the timbre quality of the instrument to be simulated.

Examples of two waveshaping networks that will be found in electronic organs are illustrated in Fig. 1-9. These filter networks consist of both R-C and L-C circuits. Applying a complex waveform (one rich in harmonic content) to these filter networks will attenuate certain harmonics within the waveform, but will allow other harmonics to pass with little or no attenuation. In this way, the waveform can be altered to produce the desired tonal effect.

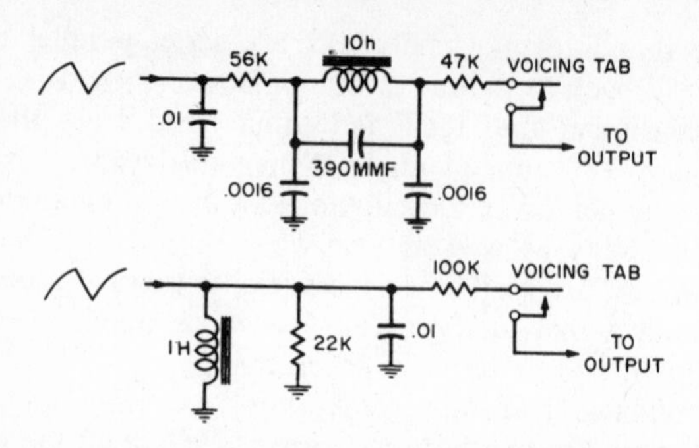

Fig. 1-9. Typical waveshaping networks.

The output from all voicing circuits feeds into a common amplifier. The proper performance of this amplifier is of utmost importance in the over-all quality of the instrument. Primarily, a conventional amplifier is used which must be capable of high-quality audio reproduction. In some instances, the amplifier may contain two channels, for separate reproduction of the high and low frequencies.

The frequencies handled by the audio system will be quite broad; therefore, the amplifier must be capable of reproducing almost the entire audio spectrum.

Although the highest note on the average electronic organ will not be much beyond 5,000 cycles per second, other factors have to be considered. The complex tones derived from a combination of tones require some consideration when designing an amplifier for an organ. As any combination of tones is played, a resultant tone with a resultant waveform is heard. This waveform may contain many harmonics and overtones which range from their fundamental, to and above the audio range. All of these must be reproduced, otherwise, the sound quality of the instrument will suffer. Table 1-1 gives the approximate frequency of each note in the seven octaves used in most electronic organs.

Table 1-1. Notes of seven octaves as expressed in frequency (cps).

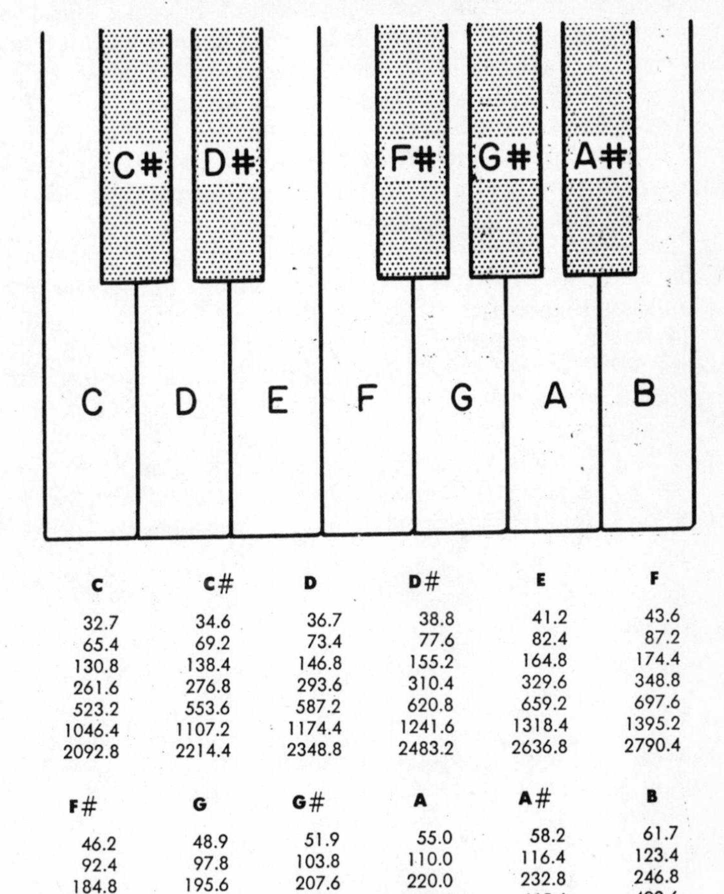

C	C#	D	D#	E	F
32.7	34.6	36.7	38.8	41.2	43.6
65.4	69.2	73.4	77.6	82.4	87.2
130.8	138.4	146.8	155.2	164.8	174.4
261.6	276.8	293.6	310.4	329.6	348.8
523.2	553.6	587.2	620.8	659.2	697.6
1046.4	1107.2	1174.4	1241.6	1318.4	1395.2
2092.8	2214.4	2348.8	2483.2	2636.8	2790.4

F#	G	G#	A	A#	B
46.2	48.9	51.9	55.0	58.2	61.7
92.4	97.8	103.8	110.0	116.4	123.4
184.8	195.6	207.6	220.0	232.8	246.8
369.6	391.2	415.2	440.0	465.6	493.6
739.2	782.4	830.4	880.0	931.2	987.2
1478.4	1564.8	1660.8	1760.0	1862.4	1974.4
2956.8	3129.6	3321.6	3520.0	3724.8	3948.8

Power-handling ability will also require some consideration in the design of the amplifier. Since the organ of today is a consumer item, sufficient audio power output must be provided for any application or occasion. Most organs have an audio power output ranging from 25 to 50 watts, depending on the design.

The speakers, which are driven by the power amplifier, may vary in size from six to fifteen inches. If a single amplifier is employed for the entire audio frequencies, a crossover network may be utilized.

If it is necessary to replace a speaker, an exact replacement should be made. If one is not readily available, the service technician should make a careful selection, paying particular attention to the frequency response, impedance, and power-handling capabilities. With electrodynamic speakers, the field-coil resistance and impedance of the replacement must be exactly the same as those of the original.

A simple means of checking for proper operation of the audio and speaker systems is to sound a bass chord at full volume, and listen for audio break-up or mechanical rattle within the speakers.

CHAPTER 2

Tone Generators

Most organs employ electronic tone generators utilizing either vacuum tubes or transistors in an oscillator circuit. In some cases, however, a mechanical-type of tone generator is employed.

Courtesy Hammond Organ Company.

Fig. 2-1. Rear view of the Hammond Model M-100.

MECHANICAL TONE GENERATORS

Hammond

In the Hammond L-100 and M-100 (Fig. 2-1) Series organs, mechanical tone wheels are used to derive electrical impulses. A close examination of the tone wheel (Fig. 2-2) reveals uniform irregularities around the edge. During rotation, the edge of the wheel is driven past a coil wound on the end of a permanent bar magnet. The irregularities around the edge of the wheel cause a disturbance in the established magnetic field, inducing a small AC voltage in the coil. After a certain amount of waveshaping, this voltage may be used as a tone. Its frequency falls within the chromatic scale and its pitch is predetermined by the number of variations per second produced by the rotating tone wheel.

Output voltages from the various tone generators are fed to keyswitches where they may be combined to duplicate the sound of almost any existing musical instrument.

To maintain frequency stability, the tone wheel must rotate at a constant speed. This is accomplished by two motors employed

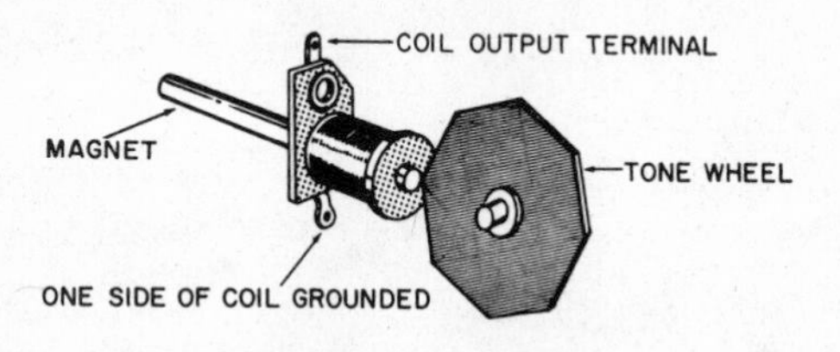

Fig. 2-2. A mechanical tone generator.

in the driving mechanism. The tone wheels are mounted on one long driveshaft which has a motor connected at each end. One is a starting motor used to move the tone wheels up to their synchronous running speed; the other is a synchronous motor that is switched in to hold the speed of the driveshaft in step with the power line frequency. Resilient couplings from motor to driveshaft absorb the small, instantaneous changes in speed resulting from line frequency variations.

ELECTRONIC TONE GENERATORS

Probably the most common electronic tone generator is the frequency divider (Fig. 2-18 at end of chapter). Before discussing its circuitry, however, let us consider its principle of operation.

Referring back to the frequency chart in Table 1-1, notice the exact division by twos down the entire *A* segment. The block diagram in Fig. 2-3 shows how frequency division is accomplished.

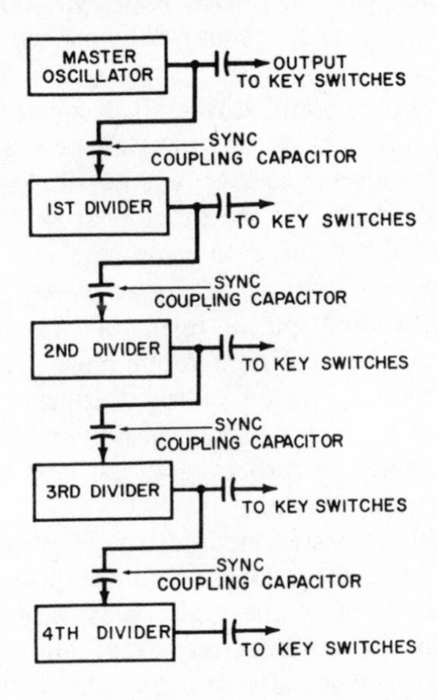

Fig. 2-3. Block diagram of a typical frequency divider system.

Although only 4 dividers are represented, any number can be used. The master oscillator, represented by the uppermost block on the drawing, produces one note of the scale in the highest octave of the keyboard. This signal is fed to the key switches of the organ and a portion is used to synchronize the first divider to the master-oscillator frequency at a ratio of 2:1.

In turn, the output from each divider circuit feeds the key switches and is used to synchronize the succeeding divider at a ratio of 2:1. This method is used throughout the chromatic scale, so that each note is represented by a master oscillator. This oscillator provides the basic frequency for all identical notes; all *G* notes, for example, originate from the same oscillator.

Baldwin models 46C and 46H, Lowrey, Thomas, and Magnavox all use this system of frequency division, with minor variations in circuitry.

Magnavox, Thomas, and Lowrey use master oscillators working into Eccles-Jordan divider circuits. This circuit is similar to the basic multivibrator circuit, except it is not free-running. Since one tube is biased to cut off and the other near saturation, it is necessary to inject a voltage pulse to overcome the cut-off condition. The output of this circuit is a square wave. In Eccles-Jordan divider circuits, one input pulse "turns on" the section from which the output is taken and the next input pulse "turns off" this section. This action results in an output frequency one half that of the input signal. The master oscillator supplies the trigger pulse to the first divider, which in turn triggers the next divider, and so on throughout the entire system.

This is a highly desirable method from the standpoint of tuning the instrument. Since the master oscillator provides the reference frequency for one note of the scale, it is only necessary to tune this oscillator to the correct frequency, and the corresponding note in each octave will automatically fall in tune.

Baldwin

For example, to tune *C* on the Baldwin 46C or 46H, we

tune the master *C* oscillator, and provided each divider circuit is functioning as it should, all *C* notes in the organ lock into their correct frequency.

When servicing this type of tone-generating system, one important factor should be considered. Each divider must have sync applied to its input before oscillation occurs; thus, if sync is lost, the oscillator will not function — and if one divider ceases to function, all dividers beyond it also become inoperative. Troubleshooting such a circuit then becomes a simple matter: find the last operating tone and check the divider to which it is associated.

A portion of the Baldwin tone generator is shown in Fig. 2-4. The master oscillator and divider illustrated in this schematic are

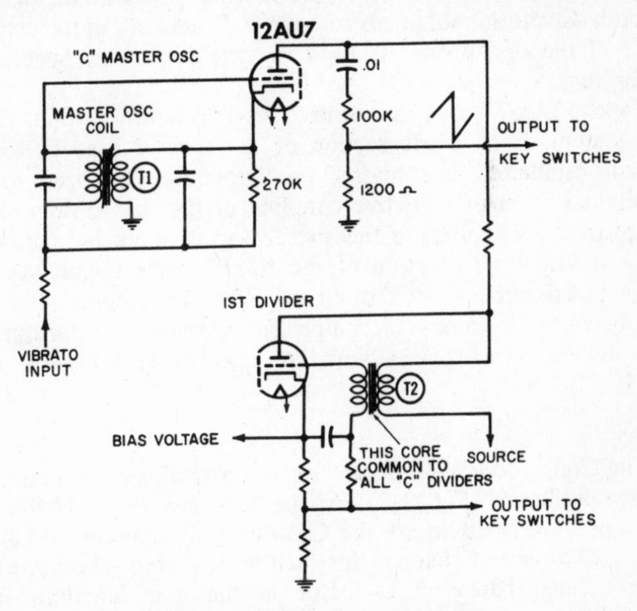

Fig. 2-4. A Baldwin tone generator circuit.

representative of the entire generating system. The only variations are in the components themselves and in the operating frequency.

A stable tuned-grid oscillator is used as the master oscillator at the uppermost pitch of each note. It employs low tolerance com-

A stable tuned-grid oscillator is used as the master oscillator at the uppermost pitch of each note. It is tuned by varying the air gap in transformer T1.

As in other divider circuits, proper tuning of each note is accomplished by tuning the master oscillator. Due to the RF network connected from the plate of the master oscillator to ground, the output waveform is a sawtooth. This provides an excellent pulse for synchronizing the first divider as well as an output of harmonic content for the voicing circuits. An identical sawtooth waveform, obtained from the R-C network in the cathode circuit of the first divider is used to synchronize the succeeding divider stage.

Type 12AU7 tubes are utilized in the Baldwin tone generating system. Each triode section of the tube is used as an individual oscillator. The master oscillator provides sync to the first divider through inductive coupling of the first divider transformer (T2). Coupling to the succeeding dividers is maintained by the physical construction of the transformers themselves. All divider-tuned circuits are wound on a common core; thus coupling between dividers is accomplished through the transformer. Each divider synchronizes with its injected signal at a ratio of 2:1.

Conn

The Conn Model 540 organ employs a modified version of the Hartley oscillator (Fig. 2-5) for the tone generator. Unlike the organs previously discussed, the Conn uses an individual oscillator (Fig. 2-17 at end of chapter) for each basic note on the keyboard, which means that each oscillator in the unit functions independently.

To stabilize the tone generators, voltage regulation is maintained throughout the entire generating system. The voltage source for the plates of the oscillator tubes is clamped by the 36-volt

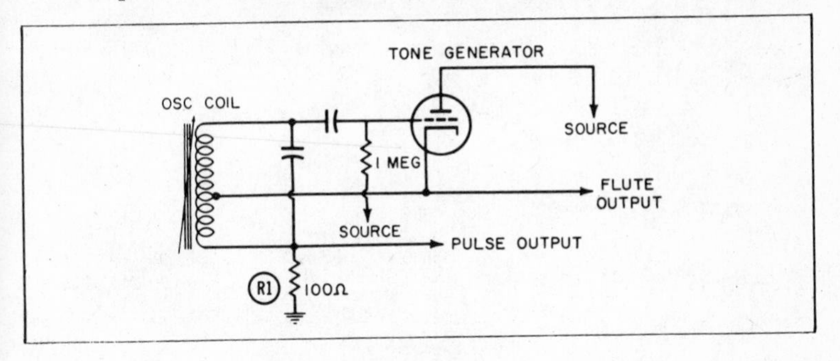

Fig. 2-5. A Conn tone generator circuit.

regulated line derived from the generator voltage regulator located within the power supply.

Note that the tuned circuit employed in this oscillator has a tap located just off the center of the transformer. This permits two output signals to be taken from the transformer. One output, almost a pure sine wave, taken from the feedback or cathode tap furnishes flute signals for the voicing circuits. The other output, taken off at the high side of R1, is a pulse tone which is used for the string voices.

Complete tuning for the Conn generator is a more intricate process than for the dividing-type tone generating system. With the Conn, all generators must be tuned individually. Tuning is achieved by varying the air gap of the core within the oscillator transformer.

Thomas

The Thomas model V1 utilizes the divider system to derive the necessary tones for the organ voicing. Transistors are employed

Courtesy Thomas Organ Company.

Fig. 2-6. Thomas model V-1 tone generator assembly.

throughout the generating circuit. The tone generator assembly is shown in Fig. 2-6.

The master oscillator and one divider stage are shown schematically in Fig. 2-7. The former is, in effect, a modified Hartley oscillator. Its output feeds the next divider, which in turn provides a signal to drive the next divider at a ratio of 2:1. This process is repeated throughout the system.

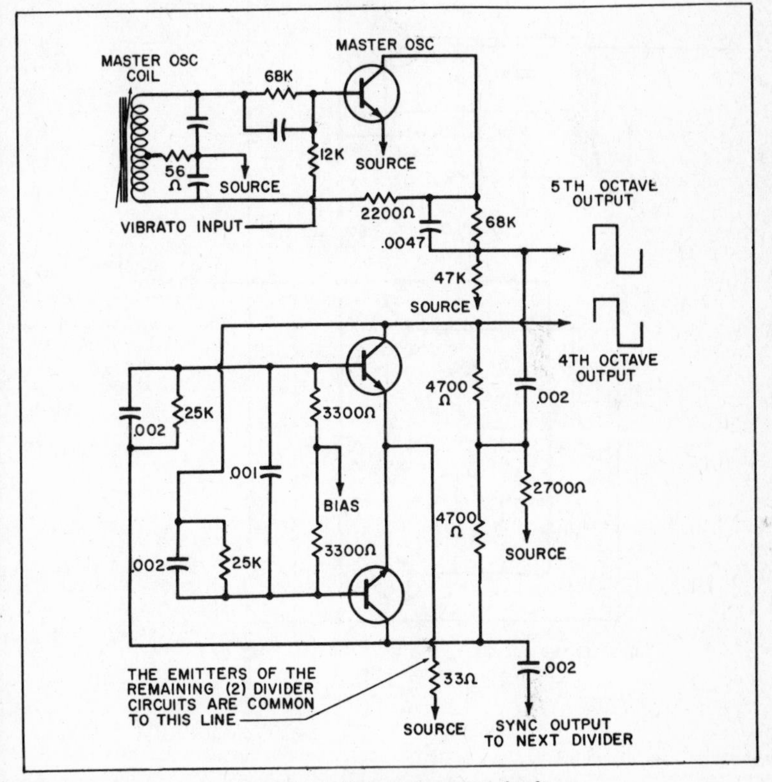

Fig. 2-7. A Thomas generator circuit.

The dividers are actually bi-stable multivibrators. Notice the similarity between this tone generator and divider circuit and that of the Baldwin Model 71 shown in Fig. 2-8. Each transistor conducts approximately the same length of time and the output waveform approaches that of a square wave.

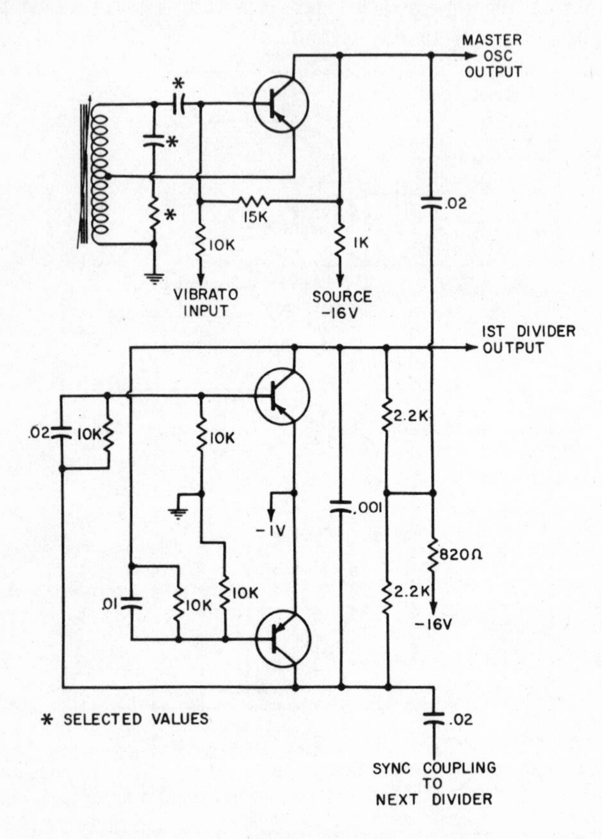

Fig. 2-8. A Baldwin tone generator circuit.

All tone generator outputs are fed to their respective key-switches where, by depressing a key in either manual, they are passed on to the voicing circuits and finally to the audio amplifiers.

Besides providing 48 tones to the manual keyboards, a portion of these tones are fed to the divider networks for the pedal-board.

Lowrey

The Lowrey Models S and LSA employ a Hartley-type master oscillator working into a bi-stable multivibrator frequency divider.

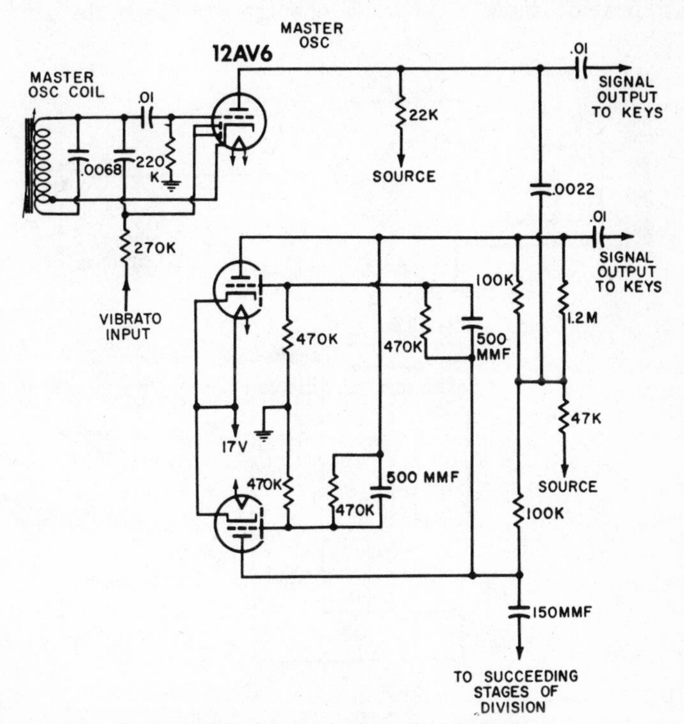

Fig. 2-9. A Lowrey tone generator circuit.

The Lowrey Model S master oscillator and a representative frequency divider are shown in Fig. 2-9.

The tone generator used in the Lowrey Model LSA differs from Model S only in the type of tubes employed and the way in which they are connected to the main organ voicing. The master oscillator and one divider circuit are shown in Fig. 2-10. A type 6X8 tube is used as the master oscillator in the Model LSA, whereas a 12AV6 is employed in the Model S.

The 6X8 is a triode and pentode enclosed in one envelope. The pentode, however, is triode-connected as far as the generator

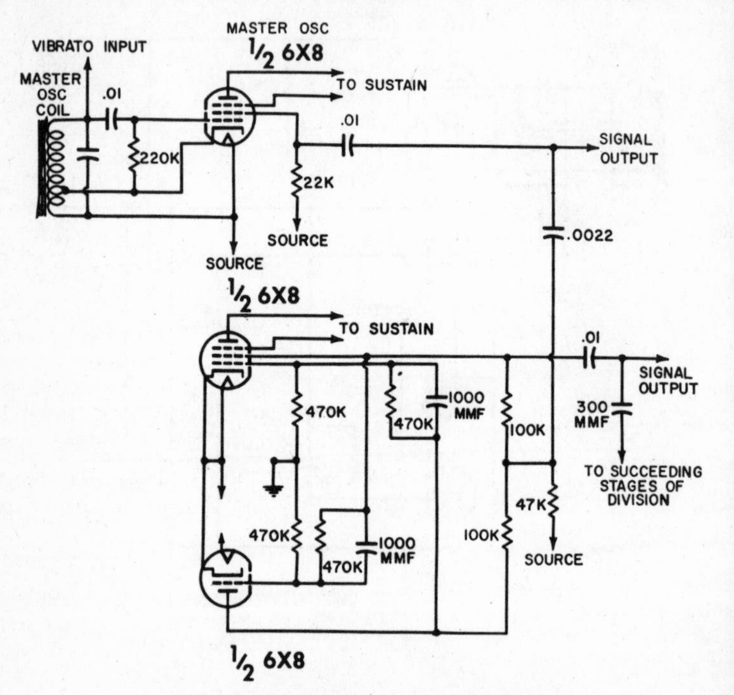

Fig. 2-10. Lowrey Model LSA tone generator circuit.

is concerned. The suppressor grid and plate of the pentode section provide the output when a sustain condition is required.

Wurlitzer

The Wurlitzer Models 4100, 4100A, 4102, 4102A, 4150 and 4150A all use frequency division similar to the others discussed, except for the divider circuit. Fig. 2-11 shows the Model 4150 electronic organ. Model numbers are very important for ordering Wurlitzer replacement parts. For models whose number contains the letter *A*, the generator assembly is constructed on a metal chassis. For other models, the electronic components that make up the tone generator are mounted on a printed board. The schematic should always be checked against the organ for production changes that may have been made during the run of a particular model.

Fig. 2-21 shows the master oscillator and one frequency divider stage used in the Wurlitzer tone-generating system. The master oscillator is a modified Hartley circuit. Its output is a complex waveform with a sharp pulse, or spike. This type waveform is rich in harmonic content—a substantial reason for its being used in this portion of the organ.

Two outputs are taken from the plate of the master oscillator. One is connected to the keyswitches and used as the non-percussion signal, which means that, for this point the signal cannot be sustained in any way. The other output is coupled through capacitor C4 and resistor R2 to the grid of the first divider.

The 12FQ8 tubes employed in the master oscillator and divider circuits are constructed somewhat differently from the conventional triode, although the 12FQ8 functions in very much the same manner. It has a common cathode and a control grid for each section; but unlike the conventional triode, each section of this tube has two anodes. This means the signal from one anode, or plate, is also present at the other plate in that section—provided the identical conditions are met in each case.

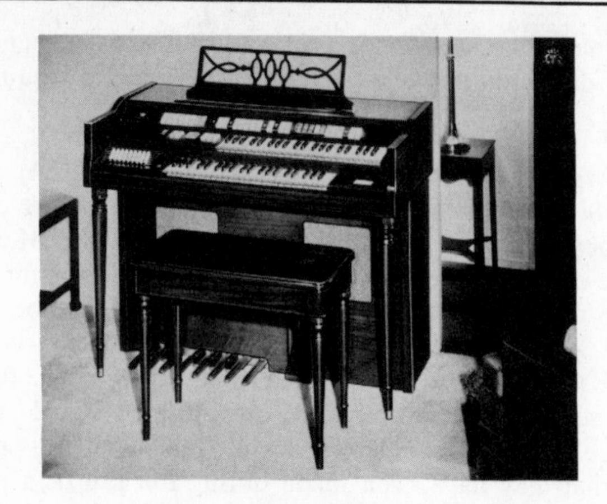

Courtesy Wurlitzer Company.

Fig. 2-11. Wurlitzer Model 4150 electronic organ.

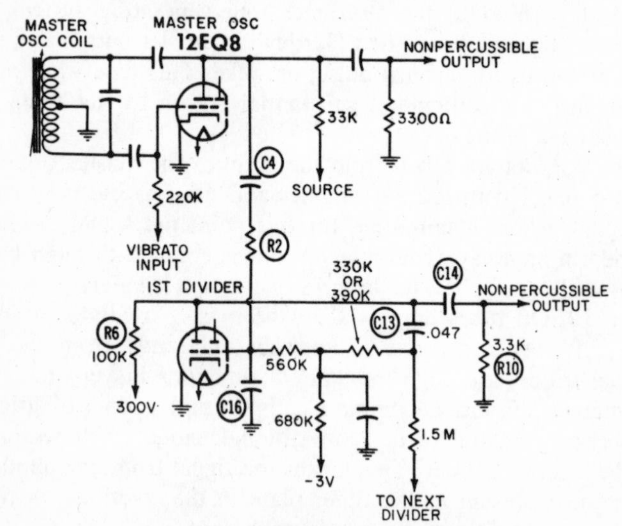

Fig. 2-12. A Wurlitzer tone generator circuit.

The divider circuit consists of the cathode, grid, and one plate in one section of the tube. The additional plate provides another take-off point for the signal, if desired.

The grid of the first divider circuit is clamped by –3 volts taken from the power supply located on the amplifier chassis. This –3 volts holds the divider in a nonconducting condition during most of the negative half cycle of the injected signal from the master oscillator. When the positive portion of the signal is applied, the –3 volt bias is overcome and the tube is allowed to conduct. C14 in Fig. 2-12, then discharges through R10 to ground. When conduction through the tube ceases, C14 charges rapidly toward the B+ value through plate load resistor R6. The negative pulse developed during recharging of C14 is coupled through C13 to a time delay network connected to the grid circuit. It then appears across C16 with sufficient delay to cancel the next positive pulse from the master oscillator. Thus, the divider circuit conducts only once for every two cycles from the master oscillator—a frequency ratio of 2:1.

The master oscillator and the frequency divider shown here are representative of those used throughout the organ; the only variance will be in the component values due to the different operating frequencies of the various circuits. The tone generator unit employed in the Wurlitzer 4100 Series organs is shown in Fig. 2-13.

Magnavox

The Magnavox Model A-10 utilizes transistors throughout the entire tone generating system. The generator assembly is constructed inside a single chassis which is located at the upper part of the console, as viewed from the rear. This type of construction makes every component in the generator assembly accessible by simply removing the rear cover from the instrument.

The master oscillator located at the top of the chassis, may be tuned without removing the rear cover (provided all circuits are

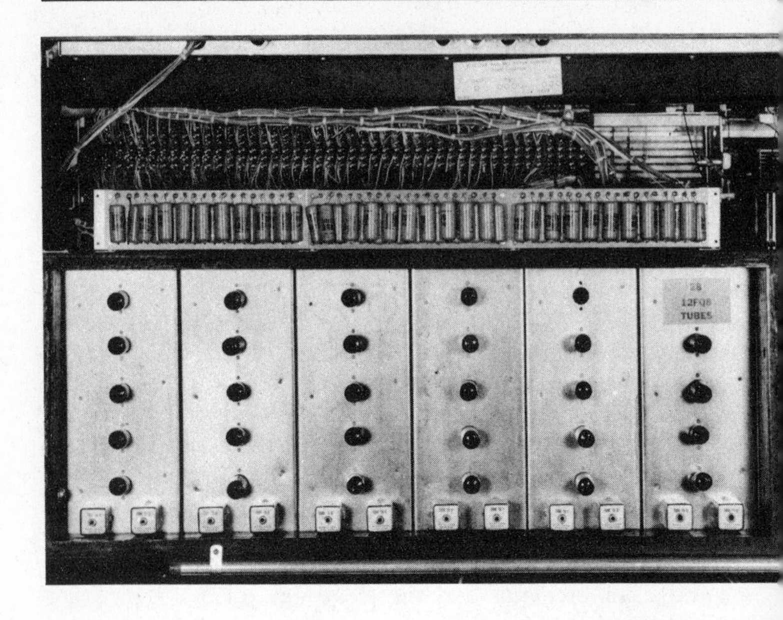

Courtesy Wurlitzer Company

Fig. 2-13. Wurlitzer 4100 series tone-generator assembly.

functioning satisfactorily); simply lift the top of the organ consol
and insert an insulated tuning wand.

The master oscillator in the Model A-10 is a Hartley typ
with its oscillating frequency determined by the values of in
ductance and the capacitance in the base circuit of the transistor
Frequency of oscillation may be varied by adjustment of th
powdered iron slug located in the oscillator coil. The master oscil
lator and first divider stages are shown in Fig. 2-14.

The divider is basically a type of relaxation oscillator. Not
that two transistors are used in this divider and that each is of
different configuration. One transistor is an *NPN* type and th

other is a *PNP,* both connected back to back in such a way that the collector of one is connected directly to the base of the other, and vice-versa.

A negative 29 volts is applied to R1 and R5. The base of transistor X2 is referenced at –14.5 volts by voltage dividers R1 and R2. The emitter-base of X2 is therefore reverse biased and non-conducting. X1 is also non-conducting, since no current is flowing through R4 and the emitter and base are both at ground potential.

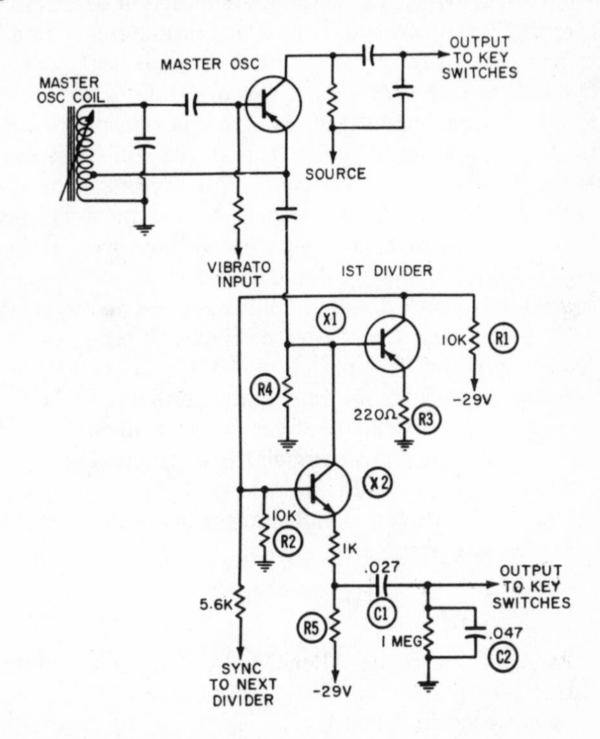

Fig. 2-14. A Magnavox tone generator circuit.

When supply voltage is applied, capacitors C1 and C2 begin charging through R5 toward –29 volts. This results in a negative voltage appearing on the emitter of X2. When it exceeds –14.5 volts, the emitter of X2 begins to draw a slight amount of current. Amplification takes place in X2 and the collector draws current through R4. This places a negative voltage on the base of X1, causing emitter current and then collector current to flow in X1, thereby effectively shunting R2. This brings the base of X2 nearer ground potential, which increases its conduction and results in a greater voltage drop across R4, thus increasing conduction in X1. The process is regenerative until C1 discharges sufficiently to cut off X2, which in turn cuts off X1, restoring the –14.5V reference voltage. C1 then recharges and the cycle is repeated.

This circuit is designed to free-run at 70% of its synchronized frequency. (The free-running frequency is dependent on the value selected for R5 in the circuit design.) A sync pulse is injected to start the cycle prematurely, thus providing precise frequency control.

The first frequency-dividing relaxation oscillator is synchronized by a pulse from the master oscillator. This pulse is capacitively coupled to the base of X1, and the amount of sync coupling is chosen to lock in the relaxation oscillator at half the frequency of the master oscillator. Sync between dividers is obtained by resistively coupling a positive pulse from the junction of R1 and R2 to succeeding stages. In later Magnavox models, capacitive coupling is used between divider stages instead of the resistive coupling discussed here.

Allen

Tone generators in the Allen Model T-44 also employ transistor oscillators to produce the desired tones. Here, *PNP*-type transistors are used in a Hartley oscillator circuit. The Allen generating system is comparable to the Conn in that an individual tone generator is contained for each note on the Solo and Accompaniment manuals.

One generator used in the Allen model T-44 is shown in Fig. 2-15. The circuit here is representative; the only variance is in the component changes that allow the generators to be tuned to the proper operating frequency.

Each note is tuned to the correct frequency by the capacitor and variable resistor connected directly across the inductance. Oscillations are sustained by feedback which is capacitively coupled from one end of the inductor to the base circuit of the transistor. The oscillator is put into operation by depressing a keyswitch on one of the manuals, which applies the necessary source voltage to the transistor.

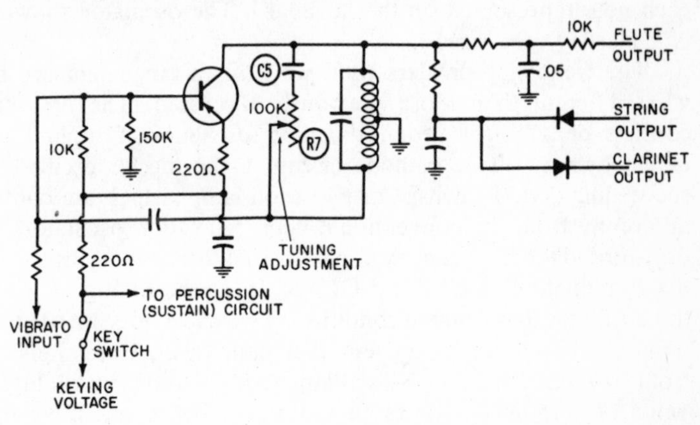

Fig. 2-15. Allen Model T-44 tone generator circuit.

Three outputs are taken from the oscillator and fed into the voicing circuits (Fig. 2-15). The Flute output is taken from the collector through an R-C network. The String and Clarinet outputs are taken indirectly from the collector through diodes and passed on to their respective voicing circuits. When Vibrato is desired, it is fed to the base of each oscillator transistor. Also each tone generator may be sustained (the tone held after release of the keyswitch) by inserting the necessary sustain circuitry into the base of the transistor.

Kinsman

The tone generator system employed in all models of the Kinsman electronic organ is illustrated in Fig. 2-16. Here, only one master oscillator and three dividers are shown. Actually, an oscillator and five dividers are needed to make a complete segment. Twelve such assemblies, one for each note on the chromatic scale, are contained within the Kinsman generator chassis. As in the other system, the master oscillator creates the highest tone for each note represented on the keyboard. The oscillator shown here is a Hartley-type circuit.

The frequency dividers used with this arrangement are somewhat different than those previously discussed. The first divider consists of a single neon relaxation oscillator. Coupling is obtained by way of the cathode circuit in the master oscillator. All succeeding dividers consist of two neon lamps which are connected differently from the conventional neon relaxation oscillator. Using the third divider as an example, two 4.7-megohm resistors and the combination of C14 and C15 compose the timing network for the oscillator free-running condition. Two capacitors are used at this point in the circuit to prevent the load, taken from the divider, from reflecting into the oscillator and causing instability. The value of C15 is ten times that of C14, hence its impedance is 1/10 that of C14. This means that most of the load reactance affecting the oscillator timing is concentrated in C14, and that the load effects across C15 are negligible. Since C14 and C15 constitute a capacitive voltage divider, there is no frequency sensitive effect; and the waveshape produced by the oscillator appears unchanged at the output point—although it has a reduced amplitude.

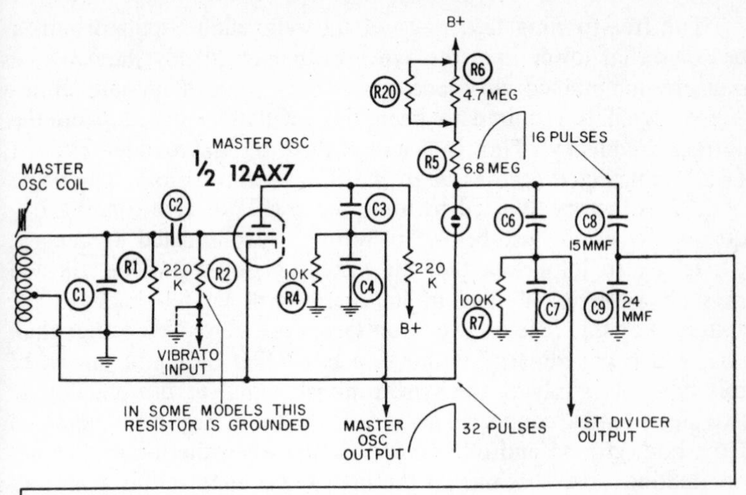

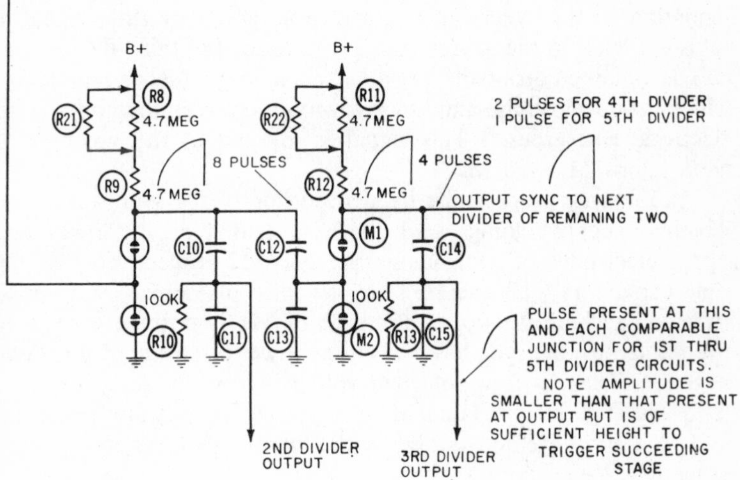

Fig. 2-16. A Kinsman tone generator circuit.

The free-running frequency of the relaxation oscillators must be somewhat lower than the synchronized frequency; however, it must be maintained close enough so only a small amount of injected signal is required to keep the oscillator operating on the correct frequency. This is accomplished by the padder resistor (R22) connected across one of the B+ series resistors. The value of R22 is factory-selected to force the oscillator free-running frequency to occur just below its normal synchronized frequency.

It is also important that the synchronizing signal be injected in such a way that none of its energy will be fed back to the source. For this reason, two neon lamps are employed rather than one, which is ordinarily found in a relaxation oscillator circuit of this type. By applying the synchronizing signal to the junction of two neon lamps connected in series, isolation may be maintained from both ground and other components, when the lamps, are not conducting. Also, because of the high impedance at this point, attenuation of the sync signal is negligible and very little signal is reflected back to the source. Sync voltage for the third divider circuit is obtained from the previous neon stage (second divider), which produces a high-amplitude sawtooth between the upper lamp electrode and ground. This signal is injected at the junction of neon lamps M1 and M2.

In the sync process, the *flyback* portion of the sync waveform, which is negative-going, weakens the potential on the lower and upper electrodes of neon lamps M1 and M2 respectively. By the time capacitors C12 and C13 (in the third divider) have charged to a point where the upper electrode of M1 is positive enough to fire the lamps, the sync has pushed the lower electrode of this lamp negative. There is now sufficient voltage across the lamp to cause it to fire. The instant lamp M1 fires, it becomes a low resistance and places voltage across M2, so the two lamps fire almost simultaneously.

If, however, the capacitors have not had time to charge during the instant the sync signal flyback occurs, the voltage across M1 will not be great enough to fire the lamp, and there will be no effect until the next flyback.

By selecting the correct sync amplitude and timing values (resistors and capacitors), the two lamps can be made to fire only once every two cycles. This is the process known as *frequency division.* Since the relationship between frequencies in notes an octave apart is exactly 2:1, we can produce all the octaves of a particular note by this method.

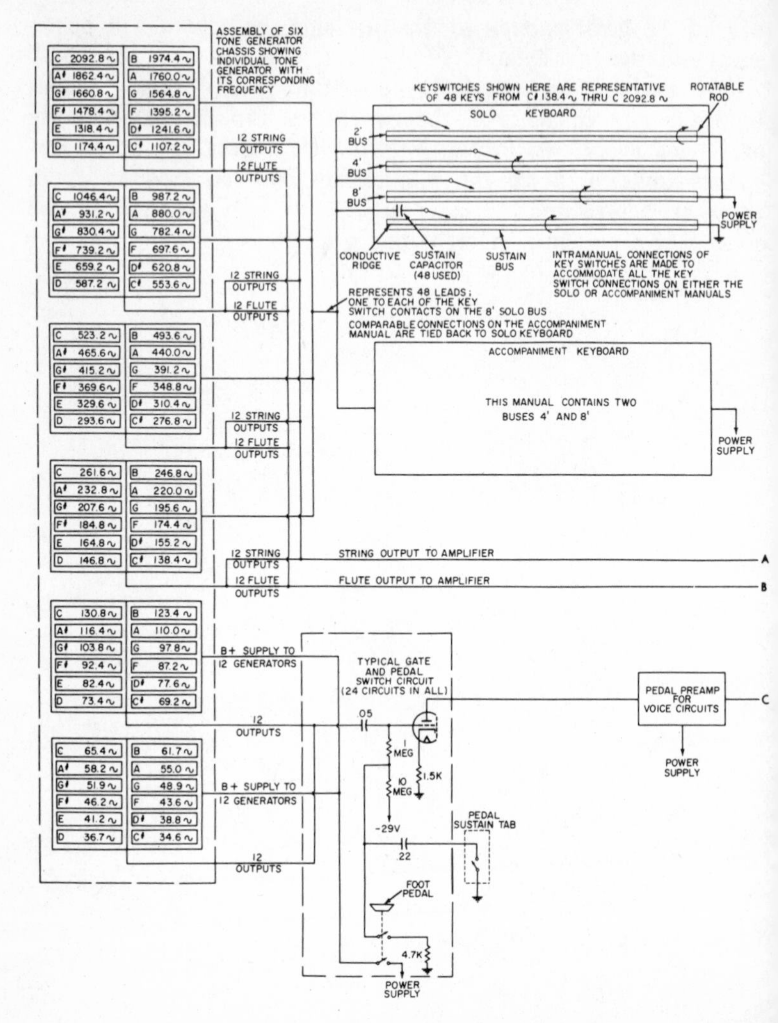

Fig. 2-17. Block diagram of typical orga

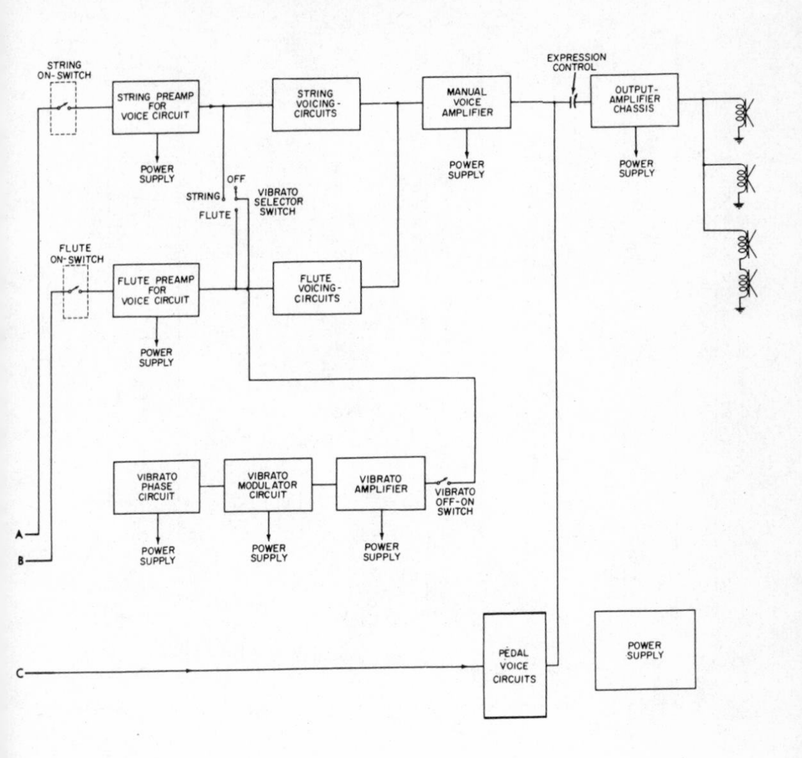

employing individual-oscillator tone generators.

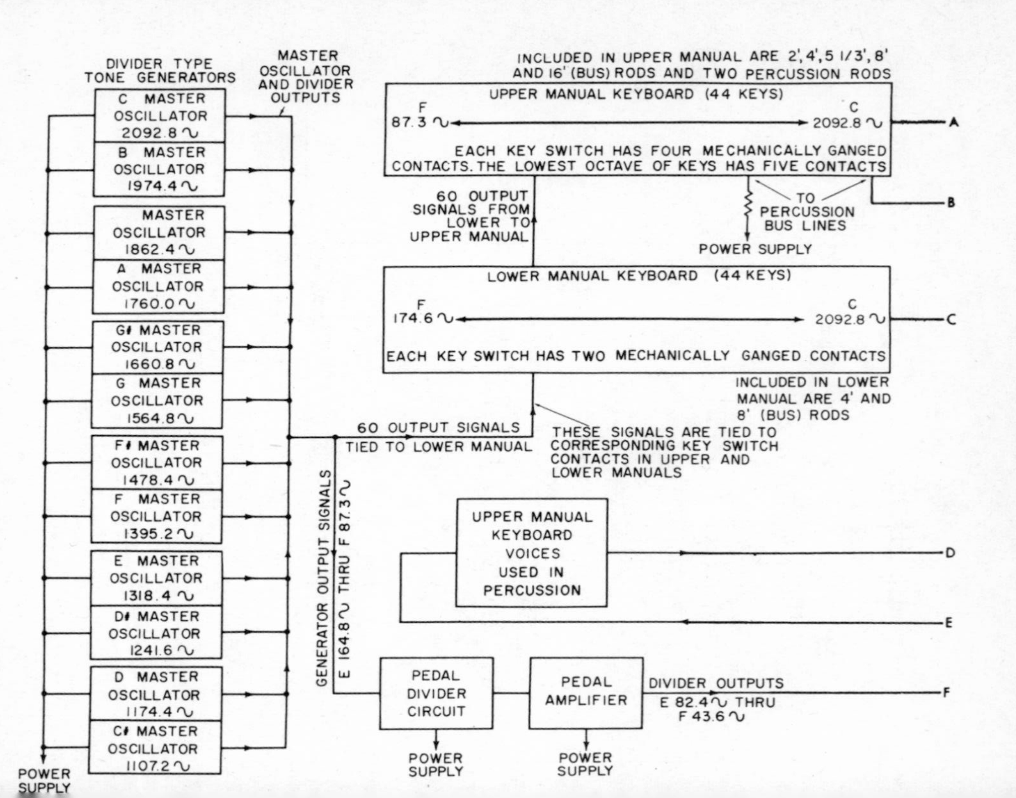

Fig. 2-18. Block diagram of typical organ employing

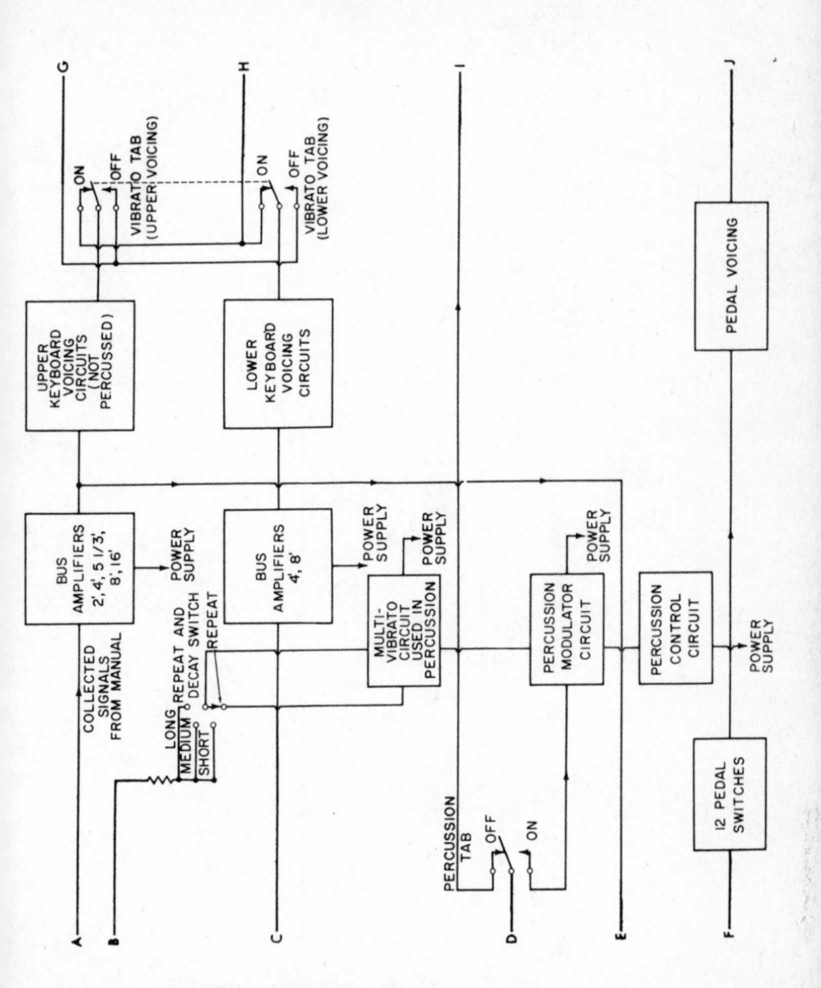

master-oscillator frequency-divider tone generators.

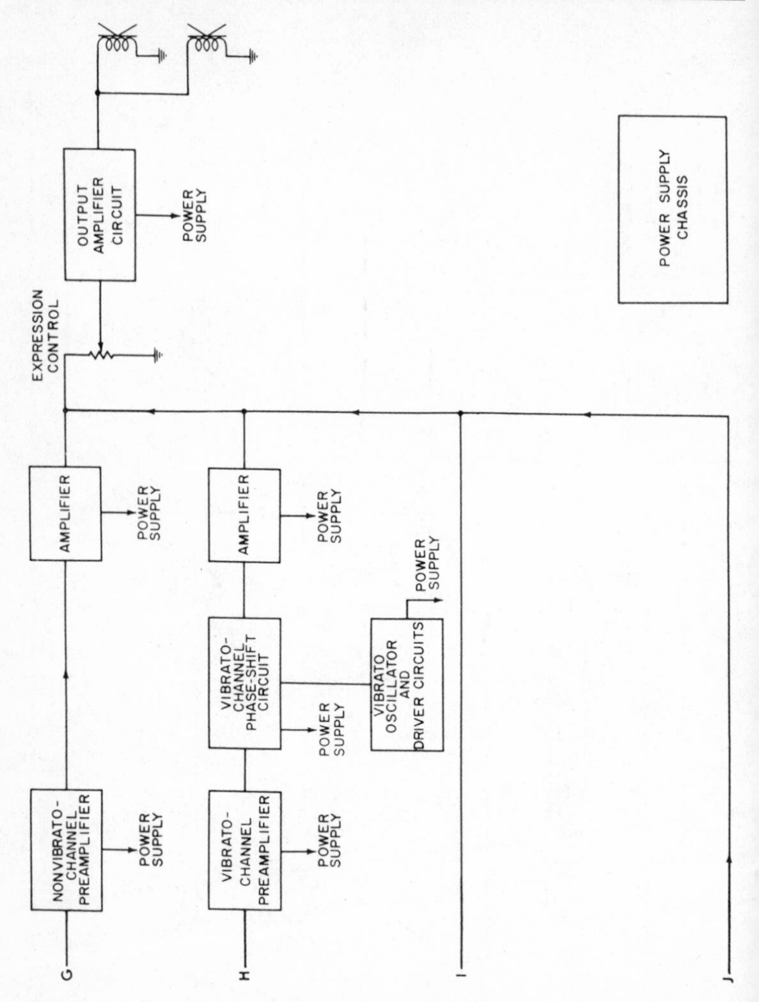

Fig. 2-18. Block diagram of typical organ employing master-oscillator frequency-divider tone generators.

CHAPTER 3

Pedal Generators And Pedal Sustain

The pedal generators produce the low bass tones played on the pedalboard. They differ from the tone generators discussed in the previous chapter only in the frequency on which they operate. The pedalboard may cover either one or two octaves.

The circuits involved range from the self-contained oscillator to the divider circuits discussed previously. The divider circuit which constitutes the pedal generator will henceforth be referred to as the pedal divider.

CONN

Pedal generators in the Conn organ consist of a single oscillator whose frequency is determined by the foot pedal that is selected. In the later Conn models, however, two oscillators are employed—one for each half of the pedal keyboard. This is made possible by the fact that only one pedal tone is played at a time; the two-tube system would not be tenable if two or more notes were to be played simultaneously. To prevent such a contingency, the foot pedals are governed either by a mechanical latching system or an electrical switch arrangement. In the Conn organ, the mechanical system is used.

The conn organ utilizes a triode oscillator in the pedal generator circuit, as shown in Fig. 3-1. In this generator circuit the

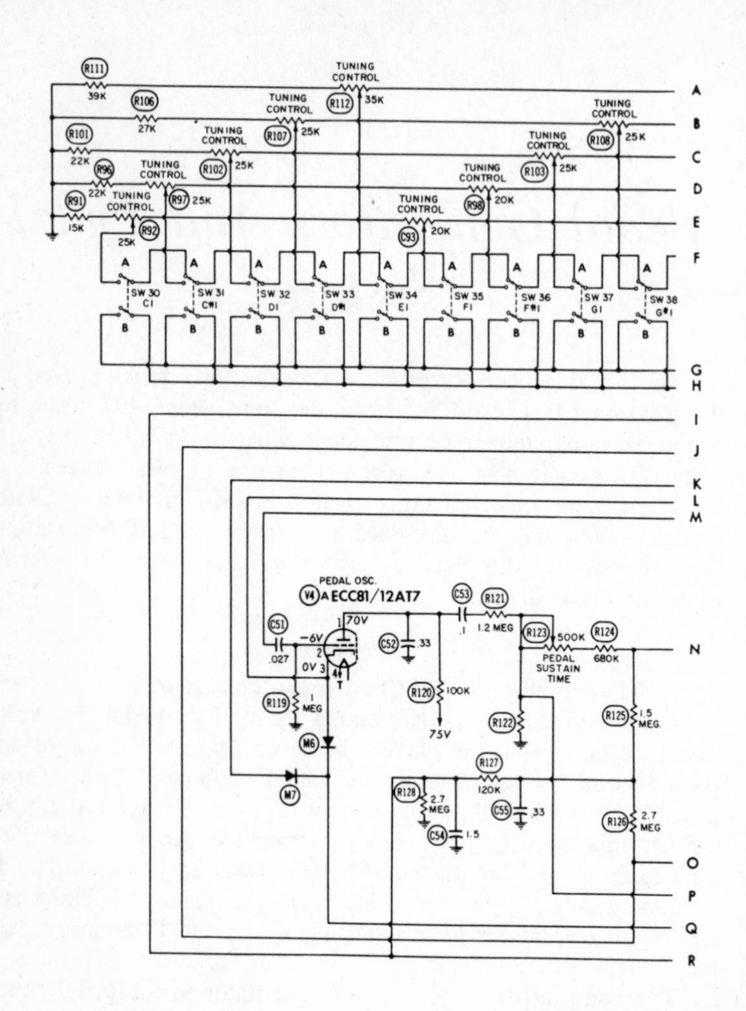

Fig. 3-1. Conn pedal

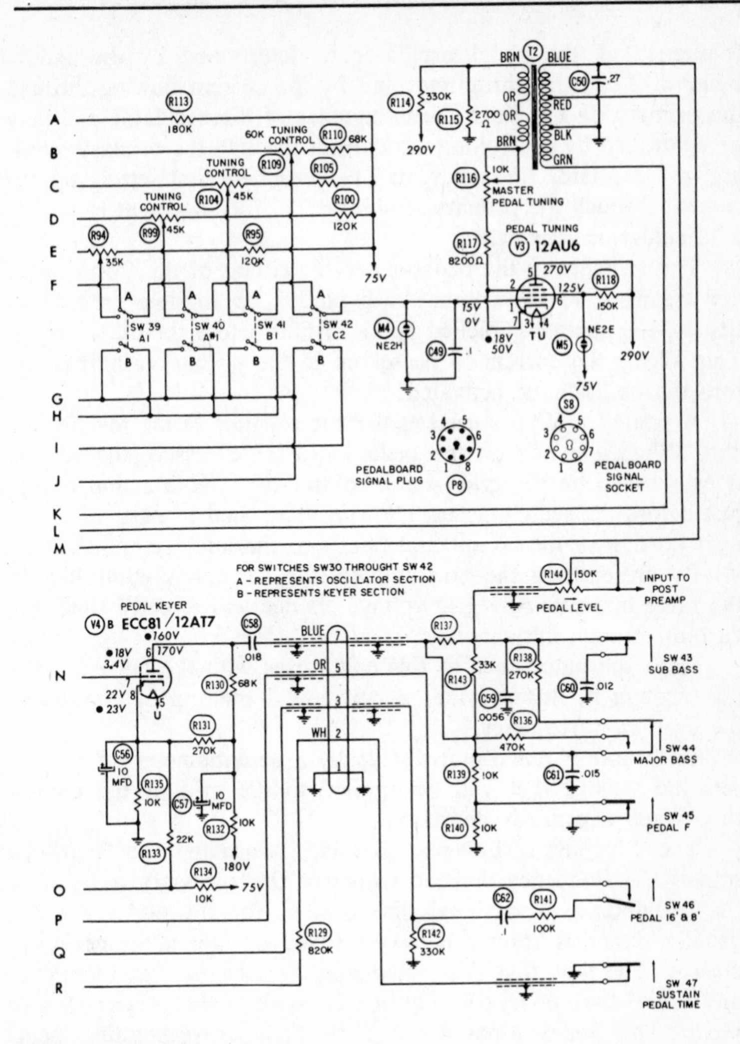

generator and switches.

frequency of the pedal oscillator is determined by the inductance of T2 in the grid circuit and by the current flowing through the primary of T2. Since the inductance of the oscillator coil may be controlled by controlling the current through the primary winding, the oscillator frequency may be preset by first setting up the current through the primary windings. This arrangement is known as a saturable reactor.

The switches in the pedal-generator circuit of the Conn organ are arranged so the contacts are picked up in delay sequence; that is, one contact is picked up an instant before the other closes. This allows the current to be set up in the primary windings before the oscillator is activated.

A pentode (V3) is used as the control tube in the reactor circuit. When a switch on the pedalboard is depressed, the voltage is established on the grid of the control tube. This action occurs just before the switch closes, allowing the signal to pass on to the next portion of the circuit and finally to the audio amplifier.

By preselecting the grid voltage, the current is controlled in the same manner. Any grid voltage change will directly affect the current through the windings.

Since the inductance of this coil varies with the current passing through it, this provides a convenient method of controlling the oscillator frequency.

Each note is tuned individually by a potentiometer which presets the voltage that will be applied to the grid of the control tube when a pedal is depressed.

The Magnavox, Lowery, Thomas, Kinsman, and Wurlitzer organs use frequency division to derive the necessary tones from the pedalboard. The signal that is used for the pedal tones is usually obtained from the lowest tones on the main generator chassis. The tone that is selected may then be divided by two or any other division that is required to achieve the proper tone or pitch. The pedal tones are fed to their corresponding pedal switches and from here are coupled to their respective voicing circuits and, in turn, to the main amplifier.

LOWREY

The pedal generators in the Lowrey organ (Fig. 3-2) are divider circuits similar to those used in the main generating circuits.

The signal to trigger the pedal divider circuits is derived from the lowest generator's tone, represented by a foot pedal. Some Lowrey models contain only thirteen pedal tones, while others have a full pedalboard extending across the bottom of the console, with as many as twenty-five tones available. This does not necessarily mean that more pedal generators are found in the organ where the divider system is used; additional tones may be added by removing signals from the main tone generators to key the pedal divider or counter circuits.

All signals are fed to a collector bus and in turn to an amplifier, which raises the signal level to provide enough amplitude to trigger the first divider circuit. All pedal signals, when actuated, are present at the output of the pedal amplifier.

Pedal dividers are composed of multivibrator circuits whose output waveform, due to the symmetrical circuitry of the multivibrator, is very close to a square waveform.

The first pedal divider is synchronized from the pedal-amplifier output signal. This amplifier furnishes the signal to synchronize the 8′ pedal divider, which in turn supplies both the signal to all the 8′ pedal voices and the keying signal to synchronize the 16′ divider circuit. (The footage here refers to the longest of a particular group of pipes, used in the pipe organ to produce the same tone.)

When selecting the 8′ pedal voice, the 16′ divider circuit is made inoperative by disconnecting the cathodes from their external bias source. This is accomplished by means of the 16′-8′

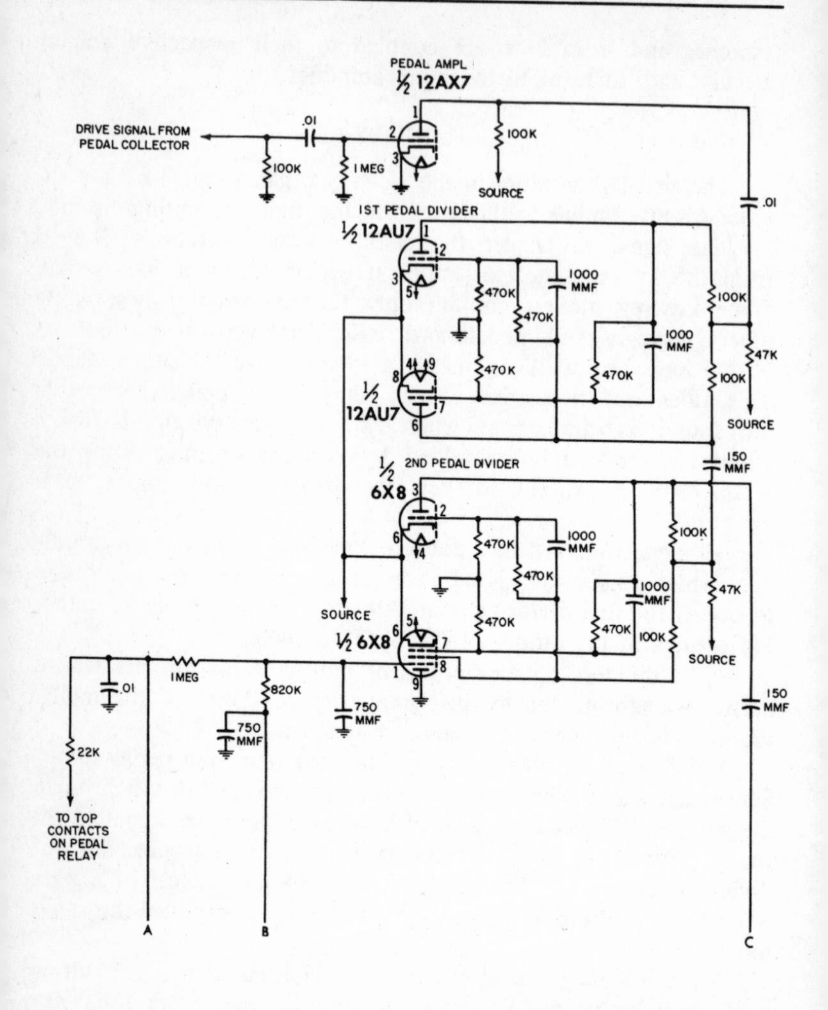

Fig. 3-2. Lowrey pedal

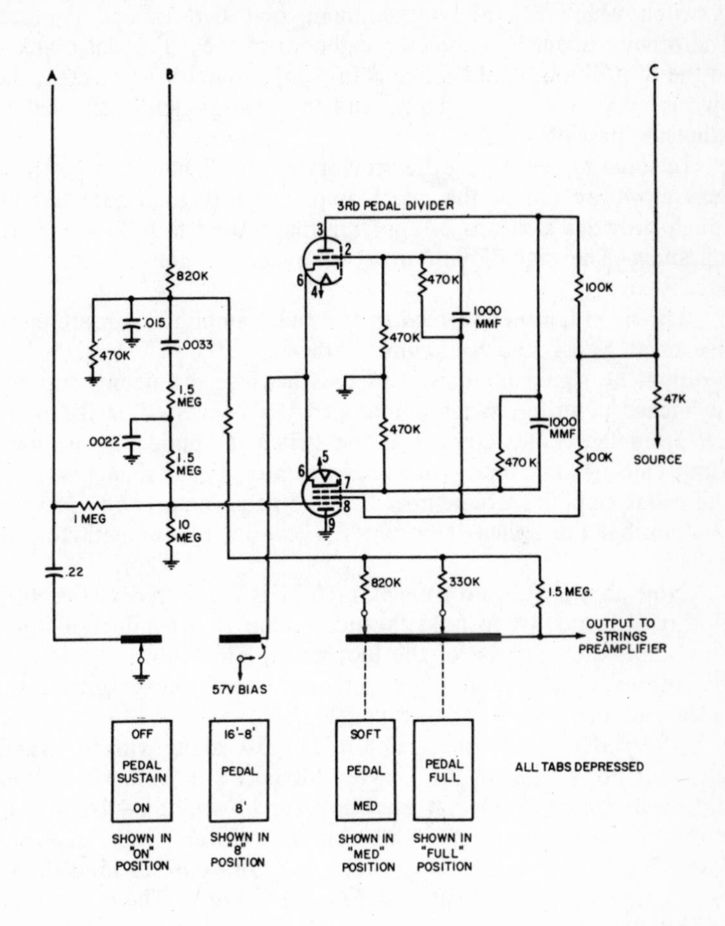
A
B
C
3RD PEDAL DIVIDER
820K
.015
470K
.0033
1.5 MEG
.0022
1.5 MEG
1 MEG
10 MEG
.22
470K
1000 MMF
470K
470K
100K
47K
1000 MMF
470 K
100K
SOURCE
820K
330K
1.5 MEG.
OUTPUT TO STRINGS PREAMPLIFIER
57V BIAS
OFF
PEDAL SUSTAIN
ON
16'-8'
PEDAL
8'
SOFT
PEDAL
MED
PEDAL FULL
ALL TABS DEPRESSED
SHOWN IN "ON" POSITION
SHOWN IN "8" POSITION
SHOWN IN "MED" POSITION
SHOWN IN "FULL" POSITION

generator.

pedal tab located on the front of the console. This tab operates a switch which has 57 volts cathode bias tied to one contact. The other contact is tied to the cathodes of the 16′ pedal divider. In the 8′ position, the bias line is broken; if the 16′ is selected, the bias is applied to the cathodes and the 16′ divider is allowed to function, passing on the 16′ tones.

In some models of the Lowrey organ, the signal from the tone generators are fed to the pedal amplifier through a gate circuit, which provides a means of applying the desired tone to the pedal amplifier. The signal path may be traced on the schematic in Fig. 3-3.

The neon lamp connected to the pedal amplifier is representative of all pedal switch circuits. With the pedal switch in the Off position, no signal is allowed to pass because the neon lamp has no means of firing. When a foot pedal is depressed, a B+ voltage from the center contact of the switch is applied to the neon lamp causing it to fire. The tone-generator signal then passes to the pedal amplifier. Remember that the neon lamp is an open circuit until it fires; then it becomes a low-impedance path for the signal.

Note that a .22-mfd capacitor (C2) is connected at the junction of R3 and R4 to hold the neon lamp into conduction for a short time after release of the foot pedal. This allows the tone to be sustained—which simply means that it will decay slowly after release of the switch (or foot pedal).

The pedal switch (illustrated in Fig. 3-4 along with its associated circuitry) used in the Lowrey Model LS is somewhat different mechanically from that used in other Lowrey models. It is no more than a spring which makes contact with three individual busbars. When activated, it does not make all contacts immediately —the first comes an instant before the second. There is a very definite reason for this. To understand it, one must trace the switch through its cycle of operation. The switch in Fig. 3-4 is shown in the Off position. Notice that the spring contact is con-

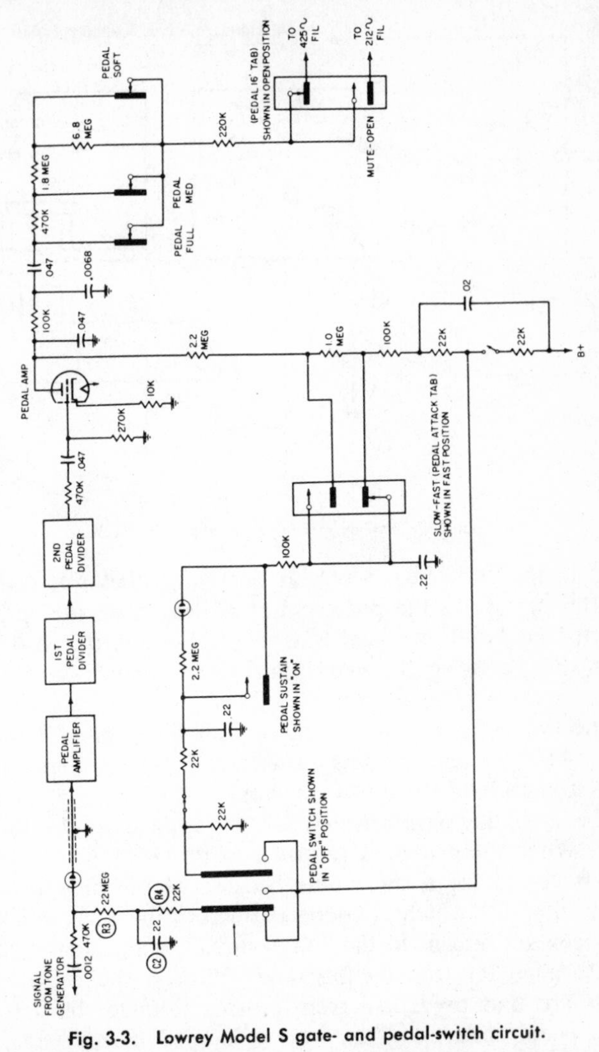

Fig. 3-3. Lowrey Model S gate- and pedal-switch circuit.

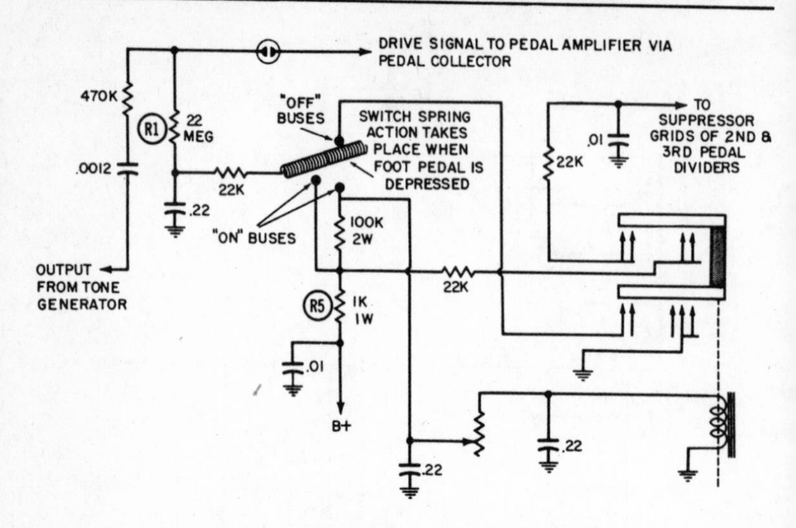

Fig. 3-4. Lowrey Model LS pedal switch circuit.

nected to the "off" bus, which at this stage does not connect to any other point. As the pedal switch is depressed, the spring first contacts the "on" bus which is connected to the B+ source through R5, causing the neon lamp to fire and capacitor C2 to charge.

The switch next makes contact with the arm of a potentiometer. At that time the relay closes and B+ is applied to the suppressor grids of the pedal dividers.

The note that was selected is now applied to the main amplifier. When the switch is returned to its Off position, the relay remains closed for a short time because of the charge taken on by capacitor C2 which is connected across the relay coil. As the spring contact returns to the "off" bus, C2, connected to the neon lamp through R1, rapidly discharges through the relay contacts. Signals are thus prevented from passing through the gate circuit to the pedal collector. This feature is used in the pedal-sustain condition so as each note is selected, the preceding one is immediately removed from the pedal-collecting bus. In this way only one tone is heard at a time.

WURLITZER

The Wurlitzer pedal generators and a portion of the pedal voicing circuits are illustrated in Fig. 3-5. This circuit operation should be studied closely; it exemplifies many of the types used in modern electronic organs. The necessary waveshaping is accomplished by R-C networks of various time constants.

The input signal for the pedal amplifier is taken from the upper manual and connected through a .01-mfd capacitor (C1) where it remains until a pedal switch is depressed. Diode M1 is reverse biased by the –21 volts applied to the anode through resistor R3.

When a pedal switch is depressed, the neon lamp fires and a negative voltage is applied to the cathode of diode M1. The diode is then forward biased permitting the signal from the manual to pass on to the pedal amplifier.

The pedal amplifier consists of a 12AX7 connected as a clipper. It provides a pulse with sufficient amplitude to force the pedal-divider circuit into conduction.

The first divider provides the 8′ pedal tones to the voicing circuits, and the signal to drive the next divider circuit into conduction.

The next circuit runs at exactly half the frequency of the input signal from the 8′ pedal divider, which allows this divider to furnish the 16′ pedal tones (every tone from the 8′ pedal divider one octave lower).

The output signal from each pedal divider is taken from one plate of the 12FQ8 and passed to the voicing switches, where the necessary waveshaping is provided. The output to the main amplifier is taken from the center arm of the Major Bass switch. At this junction, voltage-divider networks are connected to control the volume or amplitude of the signal fed to the amplifier. Manual switches

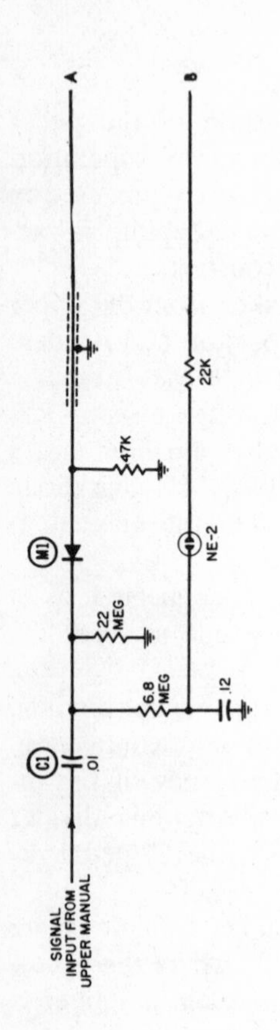

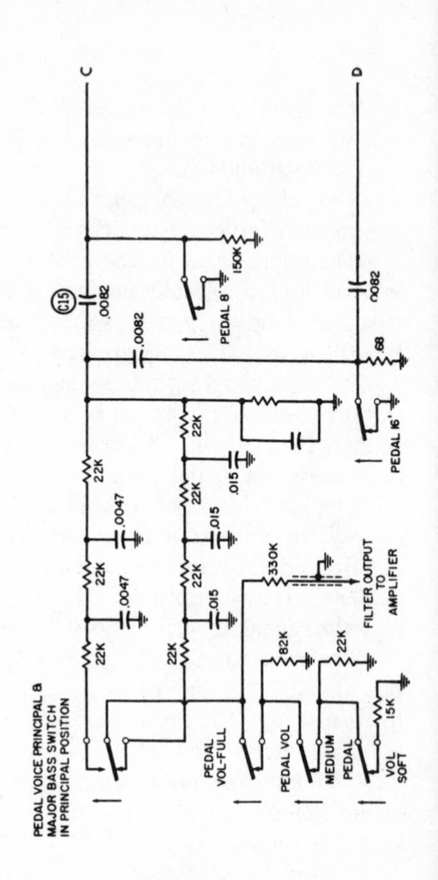

Fig. 3-5. Wurlitzer 4100 Series pedal-

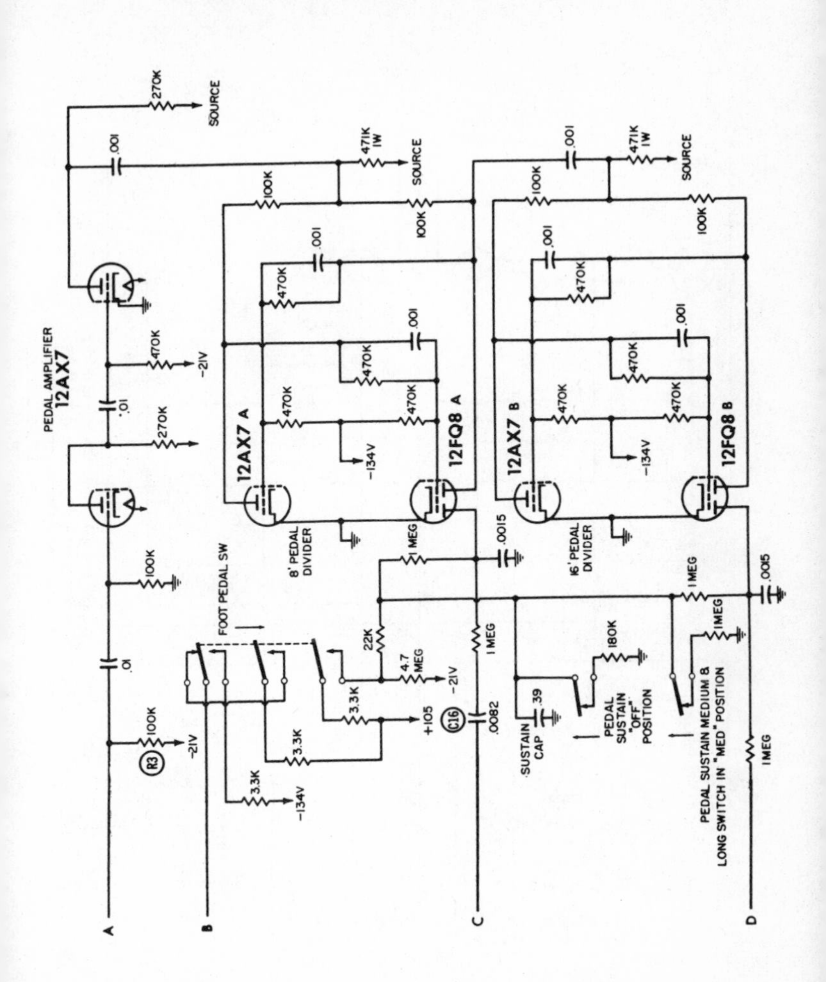

generator circuit.

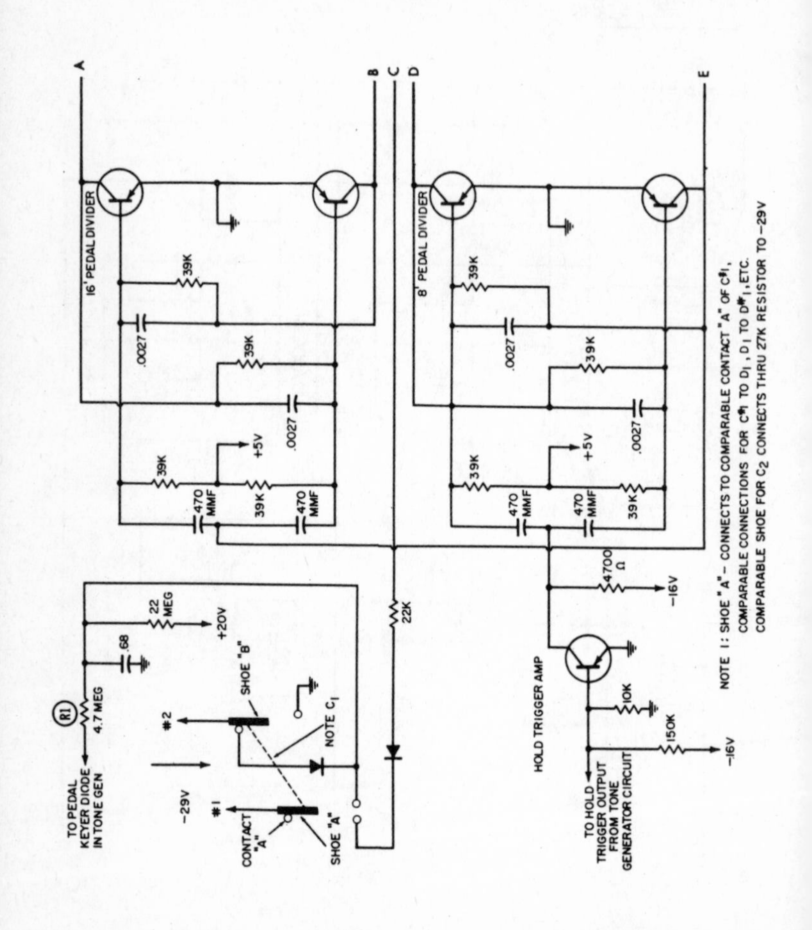

Fig. 3-6. Magnavox pedal-

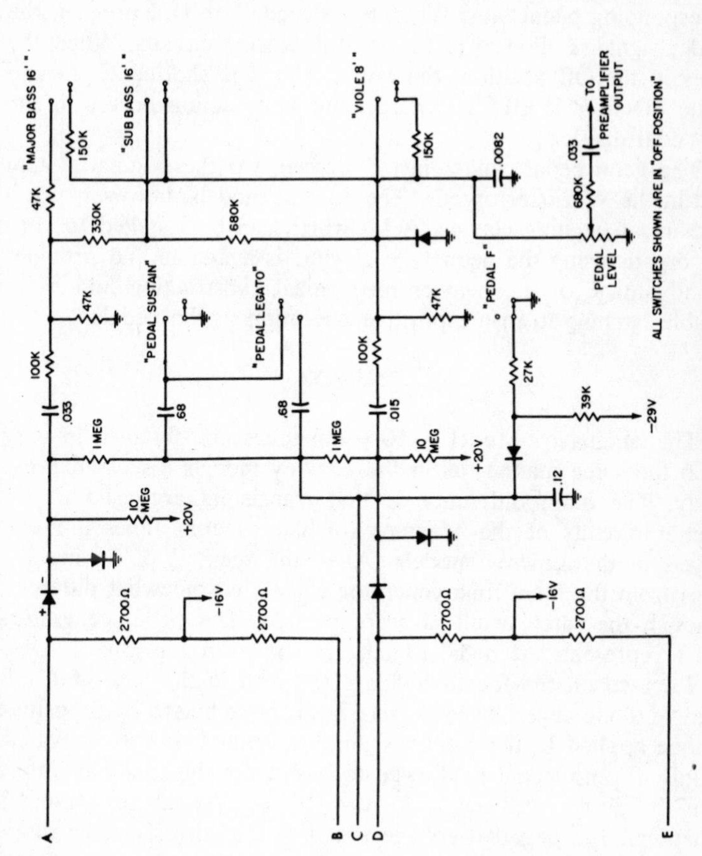

generator circuit.

are accessible so different size resistors are connected in and out of the active circuit to meet the requirements of the organist.

The 8′ and 16′ tones may be selected by depressing their corresponding pedal tabs. When the 8′ pedal tab is depressed, the divider signal is allowed to pass to the voicing circuits. When the tab is in the Off position, the output signal is shorted to ground at the junction of C15 and C16. The same action occurs in the 16′ pedal divider.

The neon pedal clavier just discussed was the original system used in the Wurlitzer organs. The current models, however, use a mechanical latching clavier. A kit which can be installed to convert organs using the neon type clavier, is available and provides the advantage of the heavier mechanical construction and more reliable latching to insure positive operation of the pedals.

MAGNAVOX

The Magnavox Model A-10 pedal tones are obtained in very much the same manner as in the Lowrey models discussed previously. The main difference is that transistors are used in the counter circuits of the Magnavox while vacuum tubes are employed in the Lowrey models. Also, the method of keying the tones from the main tone generator chassis is somewhat different, although the same result is accomplished. The pedal generators and a representative pedal switch are shown in Fig. 3-6.

Located on the fourth divider (the fifth in the case of *C*) is a single diode keyer. These keyers are reverse biased by a positive voltage applied to the cathodes, until a pedal switch is activated. In this way no signal is allowed to pass from the tone generators until the diode has become forward biased. As the pedal switch is depressed, a negative voltage is fed to the corresponding diode keyer located on the tone generator chassis. The negative voltage, applied through a 4.7-megohm resistor (R1), overcomes the positive voltage normally present at the keyer circuit. The diode then becomes forward biased and the desired tone is allowed to pass to the pedal dividers.

An R-C waveshaping network gives each pulse a spiked shape differing from the sawtooth waveform found at the output of the tone generator. With this network, the pulses decay slowly (several seconds) after the pedal is released, allowing use of a pedal sustain if desired. Next the signal is fed to a saturating trigger amplifier, biased to clip signals entering from the pedal generators.

In this manner the constant amplitude signal is removed from the output. The output is then fed to the input of the first Eccles-Jordan divider circuit, where a one-octave division occurs. This divider circuit comprises the 8′ pedal tones and supplies the trigger pulse for the next divider circuit. This circuit produces pedal tones an octave lower than its predecessors; thus, all 16′ tones are removed from the generator.

The output from each divider circuit is connected to a diode keyer similar to those utilized in the main tone generating system. These keyers receive keying voltage through the same pedal switch that originally activated the keyer in the tone generator. When these diode keyers are forward biased, the signal is allowed to pass to the pedal-voicing circuits.

In the normal nonsustain position, the time constant of the double diode keyers (connected at the output of the divider circuits) is so short that essentially no sustain is available to the pedal voices. It may be added by increasing the time constant of the diode-keyer networks. This is accomplished by adding the .68-mfd capacitors to the keyer circuit. These capacitors are connected through a switch located on the control chassis. The organist may operate them by pressing a tab located on the front of the organ.

From the diode keyers, the pedal tones are passed on to the main organ amplifier from whence they issue as audible notes of the musical scale.

THOMAS

The pedal generator in the Thomas Model V-1 is also of the divider type. Transistors are employed throughout the pedal-generating circuit and main tone-generator chassis. These pedal generators closely resemble the divider circuits used in the Magnavox Model A-10 organ discussed previously. Both are Eccles-Jordan counter circuits with output waveforms approaching a square wave. The main difference lies in the manner in which the signal is applied to the counter circuits and removed from each of the different circuits. Instead of the keyers which were used in the Magnavox models, the signal is taken directly from the collector of the pedal divider circuits.

The 8′ and 16′ pedal generators of the Thomas Model V-1 are shown in Fig. 3-7. There are eighteen tones available on the pedal keyboard, extending through one and one-half octaves.

This illustration shows the switches at either end of the pedal keyboard. Each is connected to a corresponding tone generator in the main generating system. The first twelve pedal switches are connected to the last divider stage in the tone generators, while the remaining six connect to their respective dividers on the second level of division. For example, the first *C* note on the pedal-board originates in the last divider stage in the *C* segment of tones. The second *C* note, however, originates in the divider stage preceeding the one from which the first *C* was removed. Thus, the second *C* is one octave higher than the first.

When a foot pedal is depressed, the corresponding tone is coupled to the 8′ divider circuit. A diode (M1) is connected directly to the first switch on the pedal keyboard. All tones then applied to the pedal switches, must pass this diode before reaching the first divider circuit. The diode shapes the waveform so that each signal is coupled as a sharp pulse, or spike, keying the divider into conduction. A frequency division of two is then established. The first divider furnishes all the 8′ pedal tones for the

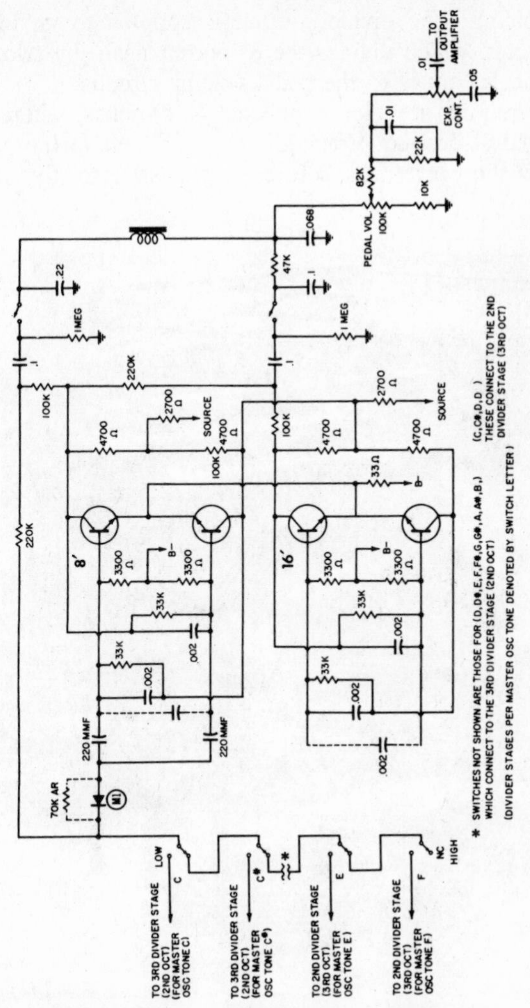

Fig. 3-7. Thomas Model V-1 pedal-generator circuit.

pedal voicing. The divider output is coupled to an identical di-vider circuit, which divides the 8′ output again by two, thus pro-viding the 16′ tones to the pedal voicing circuits.

The outputs are then connected to switches, where they may be selected as desired. Voicing is also available to the pedal tones to shape the waveform before it is passed to the main amp-lifier.

Courtesy Hammond Organ Company

Fig. 3-8. Hammond Model M-100 organ.

HAMMOND

The pedal generators in the Hammond Models M-100 (Fig. 3-8) and L-100 organs are mechanically comparable to those discussed previously in Chapter 2. This discussion will pertain to pedal switches and the pedal amplifier into which all of the desired pedal tones are fed.

The schematic of the Model M-100 pedal circuit is illustrated in Fig. 3-9. Notice that a single pedal switch is connected to each mechanical tone generator in the main generating system. All generator outputs are grounded until a pedal switch is selected. Depression of a foot pedal opens the ground contacts and connects the respective tone generator to the grid of the pedal amplifier. This tube cannot conduct, however, because of the cutoff condition established by the –22 volts applied to the control grid. Near the end of each pedal stroke a pedal keying contact, common to all pedal switches, closes, shunting a resistance from the bias point to ground and discharging the .47-mfd bias capacitor (C3). The selected note will then become audible.

On release of the foot pedal, the pedal keying contact opens and the cutoff bias is again established at the grid of the pedal amplifier. Depressing the Fast Decay tab precipitates this action due to the rapid charging of C3 through R8. Depressing the Pedal Legato tab lengthens the sustention period by adding R9 and R10 in series with R8. In this way the control grid of the pedal amplifier will not reach the cutoff point for a longer period of time because of the slow charging rate of C3.

A mechanical latching mechanism holds one contact open until another pedal is depressed. This is done in order to insure that the correct note will sound throughout the decay period.

After the selected tone has passed through the pedal amplifier, its final tone may be changed to some degree by depressing the Bass Mute tab. This tab inserts a filter network into the plate circuit of the pedal amplifier. As a result, some high frequencies are bypassed, giving the pedal notes a deeper tone.

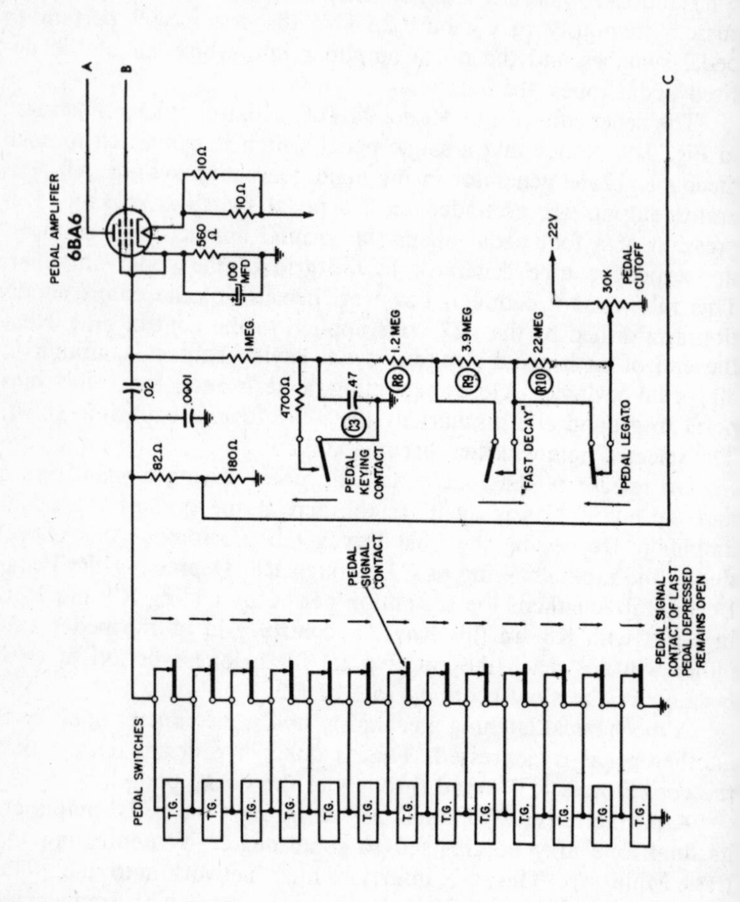

Fig. 3-9. Hammond Model M-100

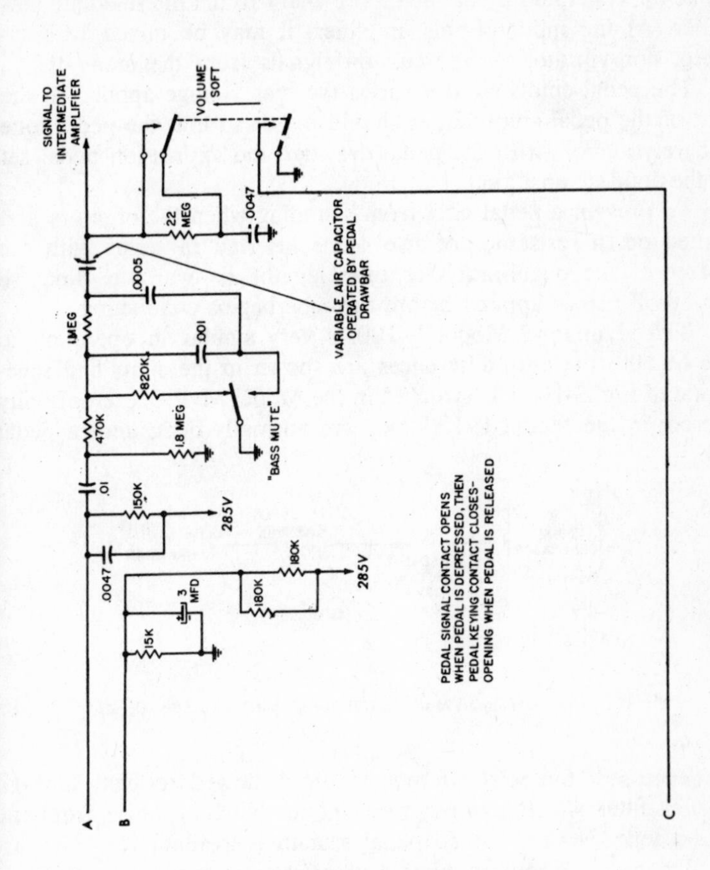

pedal switch and amplifier circuit.

The signal goes from the pedal amplifier through a variable air capacitor (operated by the pedal drawbar) to the intermediate amplifier. At the input of this amplifier, it may be mixed with vibrato, non-vibrato, and percussion signals from the manuals.

The pedal-cutoff control varies the bias voltage applied to the grid of the pedal amplifier. It should be set so that the pedal tone is barely audible with the pedal drawbar and expression pedal set in the loudest position.

To prevent a pedal note from sounding when the organ is first turned on, a resistance of five ohms inserted in series with the heater of the pedal-amplifier tube lengths its warmup time; so the cutoff bias is applied before the tube begins conducting.

The Hammond Model L-100 is very similar in operation to the M-100; the only differences are shown in the simplified schematic of Fig. 3-10. The switches in the Model M-100, are normally closed; in the Model L-100 they are normally open until a pedal

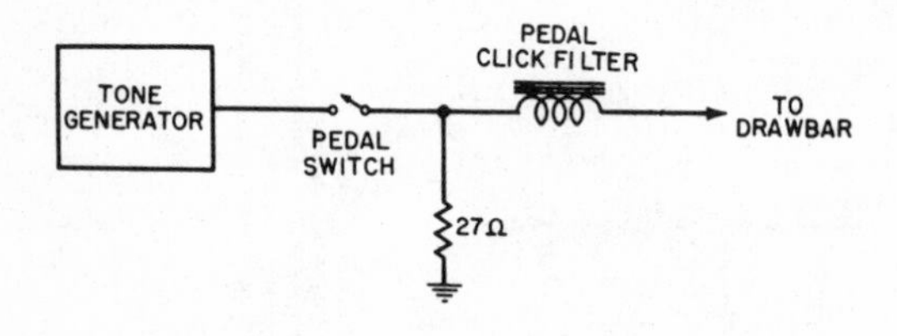

Fig. 3-10 Hammond Model L-100 pedal switch and filter circuit.

is depressed; the selected tone is then allowed to pass through a click filter which removes any undue switching noise from the pedal tone. Notice that no pedal sustain is available on this particular model. The only other distinctive feature is in the manual-amplifier connection. In the L-100, the pedal tones are mixed in the drawbars with the signals from the Solo and Accompaniment manuals.

ALLEN

The Allen Model T-44 pedal generator is represented in Fig. 3-11. A type 12AU7 tube is used as the pedal oscillator or generator. Each triode section is an individual oscillator having its preset frequency falling on C_1 and F, respectively. Fig. 3-11 represents only seven of the pedal generators used in the Model T-44. The other six are identical to them, except for the difference in component values. Tones *F#* through C_1 are represented in the schematic. The other section of the 12AU7 (not shown) produces tones from C_0 through F. (Note: A complete octave plus one *C* tone is available on the pedal clavier; thus, thirteen pedal tones reside in the generating system.)

Since only one pedal tone is played at a time, it is a simple matter to create all necessary tones from a single oscillator. In the circuit illustrated in Fig. 3-11, notice that the C_1 switch does nothing but apply plate voltage to the oscillator tube. The oscillator is preset to function on the frequency needed to produce C_1.

> **Note:** When tuning this type of circuit, it is very important that the basic operating frequency (C_1 in this case) be tuned before the other pedal generators; otherwise it will be impossible to place the other notes on their correct frequency.

The basic frequency of the oscillator is tuned by R1, the 100K control which is in series with C2 directly across the oscillator coil. All other tones are created by the same oscillator; other capacitor values, however, are placed across the coil.

Output from the pedal generators is taken from the high side of the oscillator through a diode, and passed through a level control to the pedal voicing circuits. Three tonal conditions are available on Model T-44 for the pedal tones: Major Bass, Pedal Diapason, and Pedal Dolce. Each of these tabs, when actuated, switches

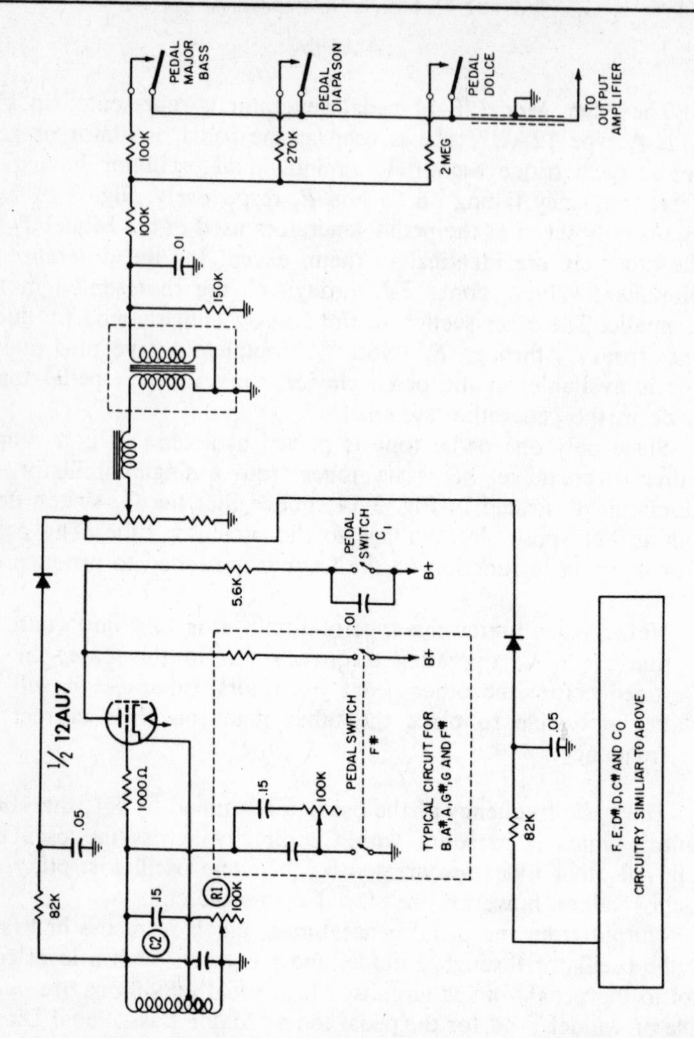

Fig. 3-11. Allen Model T-44 pedal generator and switch circuit.

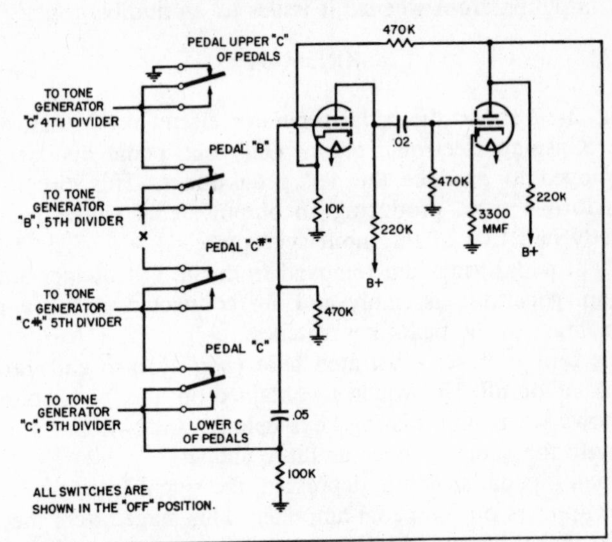

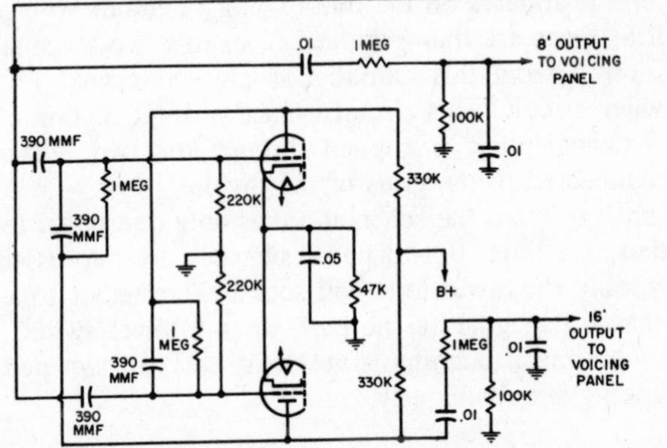

Fig: 3-12. Kinsman pedal generator circuit.

a tone composition network into the signal path of the pedal tones. The signal from the waveshaping networks is then passed to the audio amplifier, from whence it issues as an audible tone.

KINSMAN

Fig. 3-12 shows the pedal generator circuit used in all models of the Kinsman electronic organ. Only one pedal divider circuit is employed to produce the 16′ pedal tones. This circuit is an Eccles-Jordan type, producing an output signal whose frequency is exactly half that of the input sync pulse.

All 8′ pedal tones are removed from the last divider stage on the main generator assembly and are connected to the normally open contact of the pedal keyswitches.

The four switches illustrated here (two at each end) are representative of all 13 switches contained in the pedalboard; the gap shows where the missing keys belong. All switches are wired in exactly the same manner as those shown.

When a pedal switch is depressed, the signal from the selected divider appears on the pedal amplifier. This stage alters the waveform so that it appears on the output as a sawtooth voltage waveform. All 8′ tones are then removed from this two-stage amplifier.

The output from this amplifier is also connected to the 16′ pedal divider circuit. This circuit is in a normal resting condition until an external pulse is applied through the two 390-mmf capacitors connected to the grids of the divider.

It is obvious from the schematic that only one pedal tone may be sounded at a time. If two pedal switches are depressed simultaneously, only the lower tone will sound. The higher tone cannot sound because its signal has no path when a lower switch is open. Thus no mechanical latching is necessary to keep two pedal tones from sounding simultaneously.

CHAPTER 4

Vibrato And Tremolo

One of the special effects available on most larger console organs is vibrato, defined as a frequency variation of a musical tone at a slow rate, usually around 6.8 cps. Technically, vibrato designates a frequency modulation. It may be accompanied by an amplitude modulation at the modulating frequency and a pulsating change in the timbre.

Tremolo and vibrato are sometimes used synonymously because of their almost identical effect on organ output. Tremolo, however, is primarily an amplitude modulation and therefore a special case of vibrato. The term tremolo was applied to the pipe organ, where the frequency of the musical tone had to be varied mechanically. In the Conn organ part of the tremolo effect actually occurs in the phasing of the speakers, the total effect derived through a combination of electrical and mechanical means.

Although any one of many types of circuits may be used to place the vibrato effect on the output tone, the end result is always the same. In most cases, a standard oscillator circuit provides the low-frequency component applied to the tone audible as a note on the musical scale. These oscillators, whether phase-shift, multivibrator, or L-C, have much slower frequencies than the others within the organ.

Means are usually provided for varying amplitude and frequency of the associated vibrato generator or oscillator. Generally, frequency can be varied from approximately 5.7 to 6.8 cps, depending on the setting of the Vibrato Speed Selector tab on the front of the main organ console.

PHASE-SHIFT OSCILLATORS

The phase-shift oscillator is a popular circuit used to provide the low-frequency component for modulating the tone generators. This oscillator is very stable under proper conditions.

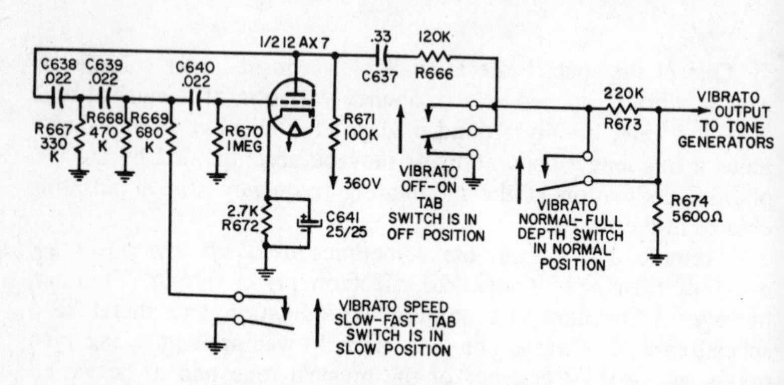

Fig. 4-1. Wurlitzer vibrato oscillator.

The Wurlitzer, Thomas, and Lowrey organs all use phase-shift oscillators. The circuits are shown schematically in Figs. 4-1, 4-2, and 4-3, respectively; notice the similarity between them. The plate circuit of each triode is coupled back to the grid through three R-C networks. Each is selected so a 180° phase shift is obtained from the feedback signal. The phase shift is 180° at one frequency only; thus, the circuit operates at only this one frequency.

Since the tube normally introduces a phase shift of 180°, the network provides another shift of approximately 180° to cause the voltage to be fed back in phase with the original grid voltage. In this manner, oscillation is sustained. The oscillations are initiated by any slight circuit change, such as plate-supply ripple or thermal agitation within the tube.

The frequency of this type oscillator may be varied by changing the R-C network values in the tube grid circuit.

WURLITZER

The Wurlitzer Vibrato circuit (Fig. 4-1) employs a low-frequency phase-shift oscillator consisting of one-half of a 12AX7. When a disturbance occurs, the slight change is amplified and inverted 180° at the plate. The feedback network consisting of C-638, C-639, R-667, R-668, R-669, R-670, and C-640, provides another shift of approximately 180° resulting in regenerative feedback.

In order to obtain a phase shift of 180° the R-C sections are placed in series. Because the reactance of a capacitor varies with frequency, the combination of the three R-C sections gives a 180° phase shift at a frequency dependent on the setting of the Vibrato Speed switch. In the "Slow" position of this switch, the frequency of the oscillator is approximately 5.7 cycles. In the "Fast" position the frequency is approximately 6.8 cycles. The output voltage of the oscillator appears across a voltage divider consisting of C-637, R-666, R-673, and R-674. The amount of control signal to be coupled to the grid of the master oscillator is selected by the position of the Vibrato Depth switch—the normal position being the lowest voltage and the full position the highest. The vibrato signal voltage varies the bias on each master oscillator, causing a frequency change.

THOMAS

The Thomas Model V-1 vibrato oscillator (Fig. 4-2) is also of the phase-shift type. The vibrato-oscillator output signal is fed to a cathode-follower amplifier before being applied to the master-oscillator tone generators.

In this Thomas model, two controls are available to the organist for controlling the frequency rate of the vibrato oscillator and the signal amplitude, sometimes called *depth* control. The Vibrato Frequency control varies the time constant of the R-C network in the feedback loop of the phase-shift oscillator and thereby changes the oscillator frequency.

The Vibrato Depth control is effectively connected to the grid of the cathode-follower stage. The prime function of this control is to change the amplitude of the driving signal fed to the grid of the cathode follower. When vibrato is not desired, a vibrato On-Off switch may be actuated to completely remove the vibrato signal from this point in the circuit by shorting the vibrato-oscillator output to ground.

The vibrato signal used to modulate the master oscillators is taken from the cathode follower through a 50-mfd electrolytic capacitor. This type of coupling is necessary because the vibrato

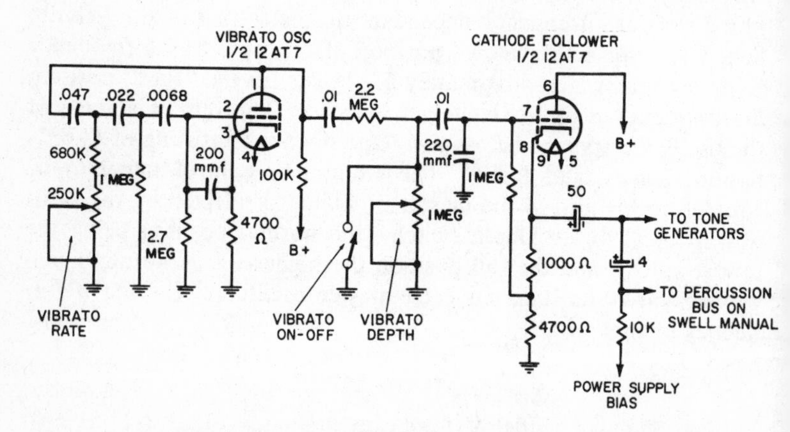

Fig. 4-2. Thomas vibrato oscillator.

signal is feeding a low-impedance load. The load, in this case, is the master oscillator transistors. Such close coupling helps to prevent phase shift at the low-frequency rate produced by the vibrato oscillator.

LOWREY

Model SS

The vibrato oscillator used in Lowrey Model SS (Fig. 4-3) provides a six cycle (approximately) pulse which produces the vibrato effect. This oscillator is similar to the vibrato oscillator used in other Lowrey models except for slight differences in component values.

The output is coupled to a cathode-follower stage. The signal is taken from this cathode follower, and applied to the diode plates located within the master oscillator tubes. A .0068-mfd capacitor is connected between the diode plate and oscillator-tank circuit of each of the 12 master oscillators. Since the cathode is common to both the diode and the triode sections, the capacitor is effectively shunted through the tube and across the tank circuit.

On positive going half cycles of voltage from the cathode follower, diode conduction is maximum and the capacitor has greatest effect on the generator frequency. As the voltage goes in the negative direction (this voltage can never become negative with respect to ground) diode conduction reduces and the capacitive effect on the frequency is lessened. Thus, the diode circuit acts as a variable resistor in series with a capacitor across the tank circuit.

The vibrato is controlled by three tabs—Off-On, Light-Heavy, and Slow-Fast. Vibrato is turned off with the Off-On tab, which grounds the output of the oscillator. With the Slow-Fast tab in the Fast position, a resistor on the tab board is added to the vibrato-oscillator feedback loop, increasing the speed. When the Light-Heavy tab is in the Light position, a resistor is added between the oscillator output and ground, decreasing the intensity.

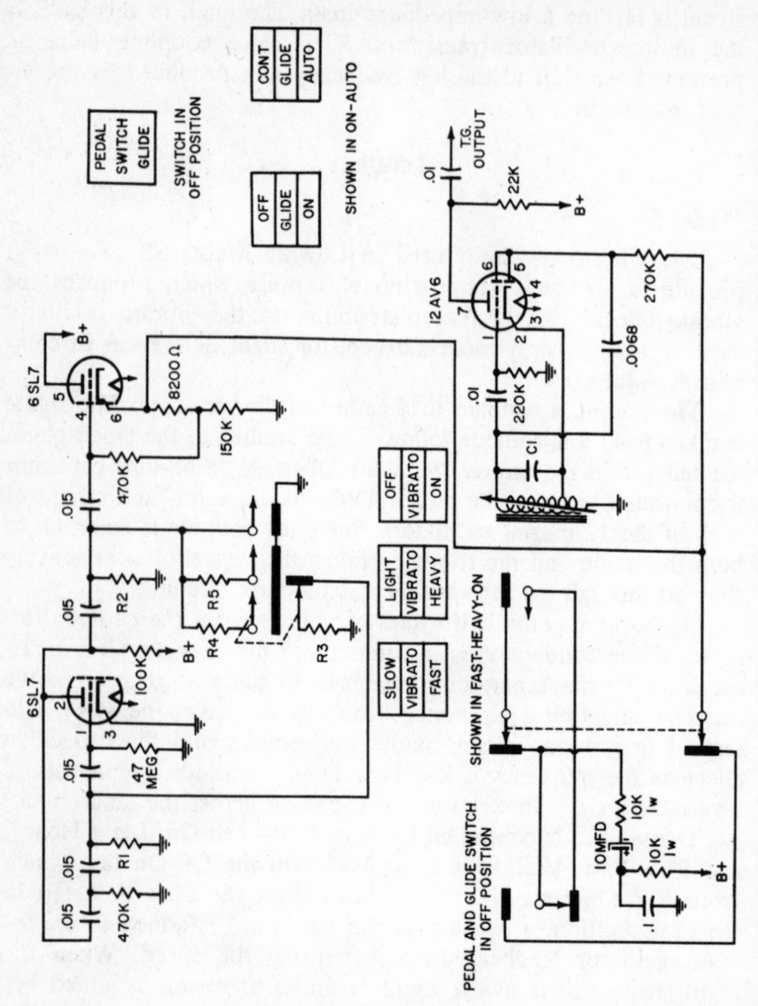

Fig. 4-3 Lowrey vibrato oscillator.

A third resistor is added to reduce intensity when in the Slow and Heavy positions.

The Glide switch (controlled by the lever on the left side of the expression pedal) found in Model SS only, when activated, applies B+ to the vibrato cathode-follower circuit, eliminating the vibrato pulse, and providing sufficient DC to cause the V1 diodes to conduct more heavily. This increases the effect of the .0082-mfd capacitor in each of the master oscillators, lowering the pitch.

This arrangement allows the organist to create special effects with the instrument by making an instantaneous change in pitch of all the organ tones.

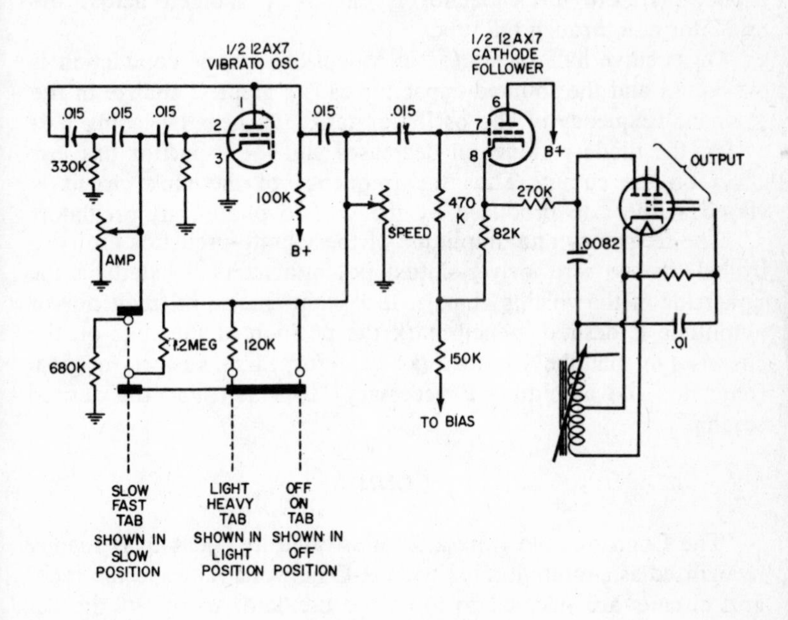

Fig. 4-4. Lowrey vibrato oscillator.

Model PS

The Lowrey Model PS utilizes a vibrato circuit somewhat different from other Lowrey models. Fig. 4-4 shows the phase-shift type oscillator employed to produce the vibrato frequency in this model. The output signal from the vibrato oscillator is capacitively coupled to a cathode-follower amplifier. The cathode-follower output is coupled to a diode plate (located in the envelope with the tone generator).

Also connected to the diode plate is a .0082-mfd capacitor, returned to one side of the tone-generator oscillator coil. The cathode is common to both the diode and the master-oscillator triode; therefore the capacitor is effectively shunted across the oscillator coil through the tube.

On positive half cycles (as in Model SS), diode conduction is maximum and the shunted capacitor causes greatest change in the resonant frequency of the oscillator tank. On negative going half cycles, the diode conduction decreases and the capacitor has less effect on the circuit. Thus the frequency of the tank circuit is varied at the rate produced by the vibrato phase-shift oscillator.

The frequency and amplitude of the vibrato-oscillator are controlled by two screwdriver-slotted potentiometers, located on the underside of the voicing chassis. If a slight change in frequency or amplitude is desired, pencil-mark the position of the slots on the chassis (so that the vibrato may be returned to near its original frequency and amplitude if necessary) then adjust to the desired setting.

CONN

The Conn tremolo generator, illustrated in Fig. 4-5, is readily recognized as a multivibrator type. R-C network values in the tube-grid circuits are selected to force the oscillator to run at the desired rate. Tremolo frequency rate in Conn organs (Fig. 4-6) ranges from approximately 5.7 to 7.2 cps. (The tremolo frequency is set at the factory and may not be adjusted manually.)

For the multivibrator, conventional load resistors are replaced with a center-tapped transformer which serves a dual purpose: it provides coupling from the tremolo generator to the tone generators, and shapes the multivibrator output waveform.

Amplitude from the tremolo generator may be controlled by tabs on the front of the organ which, when depressed, actuate contacts that switch resistors in or out of the generator-cathode

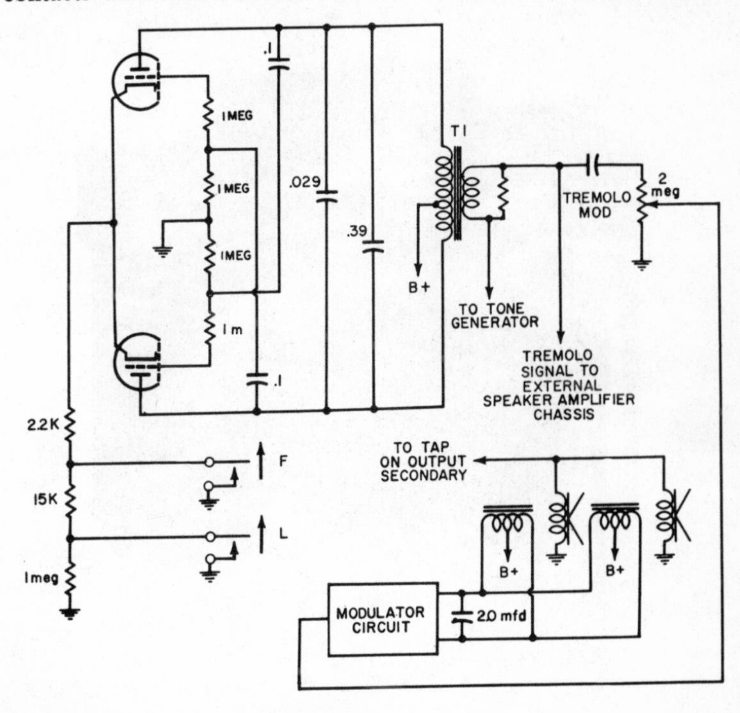

Fig. 4-5. Conn tremolo oscillator.

circuit. When both switches (F and L) are open, resistance raises the cathode voltage to the point where the tubes no longer conduct. By depressing the Tremolo L tab, the 1-megohm resistor is shorted, starting the oscillator. The generator output does not reach a maximum, however, until the Tremolo F tab is depressed. At that time the only resistance remaining in the cathode circuit is the 2.2K resistor. This decreases the cathode bias and increases the output. Because of its location in the circuit, the Tremolo F tab always overrides the Tremolo L switch.

Courtesy Conn Organ Company.

Fig. 4-6. Conn Model 540.

The output from the tremolo generator is taken across the secondary of T1 and connected through resistor networks to the tone-generator grids, where modulation of the emitted tone occurs.

The tremolo signal is also connected to another amplifier, the tremolo modulator. This modulator is designed to provide maximum gain at tremolo frequency. It provides several watts of tremolo signal for two dynamic speaker fields. Fig. 4-5 shows these speakers connected to the tremolo modulator to produce an electro-acoustical effect.

The final output tubes in the tremolo modulator are two 6L6 types connected in a push-pull arrangement; dynamic speaker field coils are connected in the plate circuits. The result of this arrangement is a continual shifting of the tremolo-signal phase within the field coils, and a cancellation and addition to the signals from the main organ speakers. Thus, the output signal from the instrument is continually varying at the tremolo rate. This is an acoustic tremolo in the sense that formation of the effect takes place between the interaction of the electrodynamic and main organ speakers. The Conn Model 540 exploits this added tremolo to provide greater effect to simulated flute voices.

BALDWIN

The Baldwin organ contains a vibrato oscillator (Fig. 4-7) different from the models discussed previously.

Model 46

The vibrato oscillator used in the Model 46 is a modified Hartley with an iron core choke comprising the inductance. The capacitance that shunts the inductance to determine the resonant frequency is selected by the manufacturer to force the circuit to oscillate at the desired vibrato rate.

Three vibrato conditions are available to the organist: Light, Medium, and Full. Depressing the Light-vibrato tab inserts a 15K

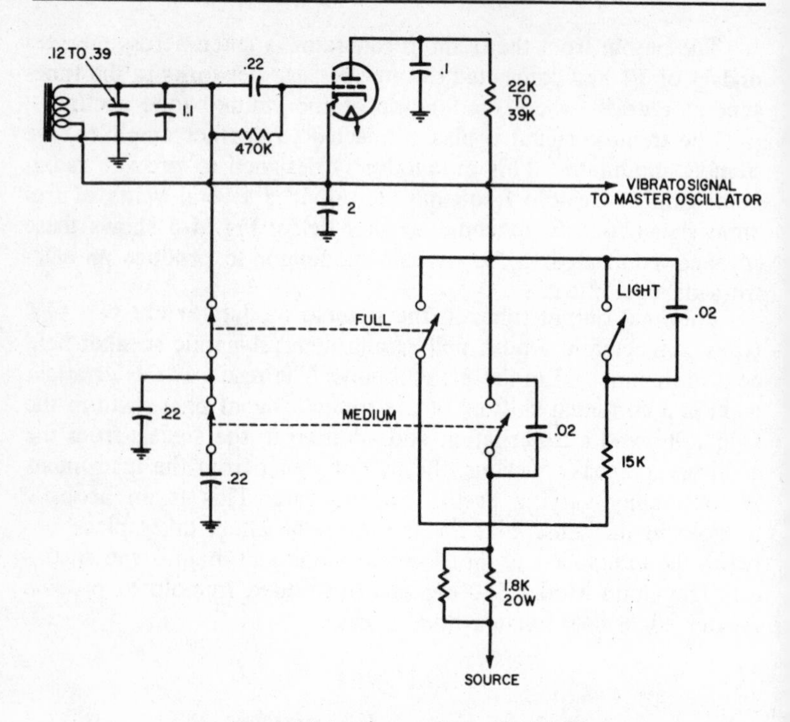

Fig. 4-7. Baldwin vibrato oscillator (Model 46).

resistor in series with the oscillator-plate load decreasing the amplitude of the cathode signal. Notice that with the Full and Medium tabs in the Off position, two .22-mfd capacitors are connected directly across the oscillator inductance. This is the normal vibrato condition.

When the Medium tab is depressed, two switch sections are actuated: one connects B+ to the plate-load resistor; the other removes one .22-mfd capacitor from the oscillator circuit. This slightly increases the vibrato rate.

Depressing the Full switch also actuates two switch sections: one is in parallel with part of the Medium Vibrato switch and places B+ on the tube plate, while the other removes both .22-mfd capacitors from the active circuit. This considerably increases the vibrato rate.

Model 71-P

The Baldwin Model 71-P (Fig. 4-8) vibrato oscillator is a phase-shift type running at a rate of approximately 6.9 cps. Transistors are utilized throughout both the oscillator and emitter follower which receives its signal

To acquire the necessary 180° phase shift, output from the vibrato amplifier is coupled to the R-C network, which again affects a 180° shift; thus a full 360° phase shift is applied to the base of the vibrato-oscillator transistor.

The vibrato-oscillator signal is then connected to an emitter follower, providing an impedance match to the transistor master oscillators used in this organ. The amplitude of the output signal may be altered slightly by the Vibrato Light and Vibrato Full tab switches. In the Vibrato Light position the signal is taken through the 1.8K resistor, while in the Vibrato Full position, this resistor is bypassed and the vibrato signal reaches a somewhat higher amplitude.

The signal is finally fed to the master oscillators in the tone generating system, where it modulates them at the vibrato rate. Each divider in turn is modulated because of the connection between master oscillator and first divider, and between adjacent dividers. In this manner all tone generators receive modulation.

The manufacturer presets the frequency of the vibrato oscillator by proper selection of R3. If it should become necessary to correct the frequency, because of a change in component values, the resistor should be chosen to place the vibrato oscillator on frequency of approximately 6.9 cps.

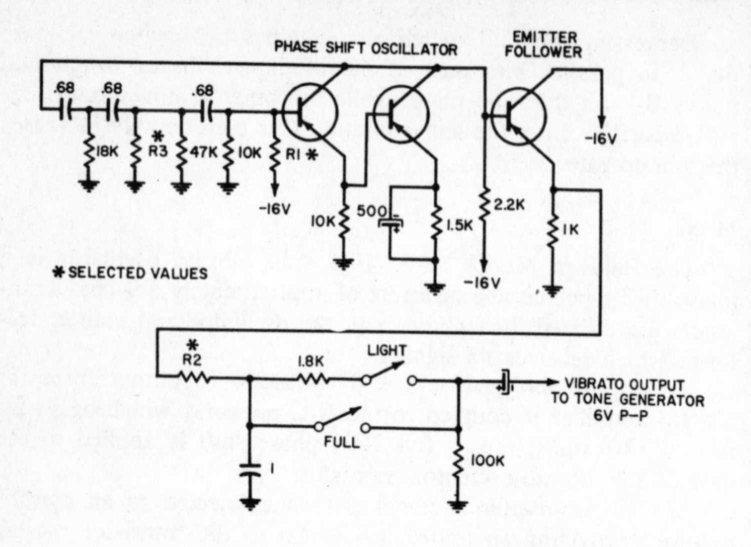

Fig. 4-8. Baldwin vibrato oscillator (Model 71).

In the same manner R2 selection is made to maintain the correct output amplitude from the emitter follower. This resistor is selected to maintain 6 volts, peak to peak, working into a 1,000-ohm load at the junction with the 1.8K resistor. Before making selection, however, be certain that a –9.5 volts exists at the collector of the vibrato oscillator. If not, different R1 resistors should be tried until one is found to establish the –9.5 volts.

MAGNAVOX

The vibrato oscillator used in the Magnavox Model A-10 is a transistor type (transistors are used exclusively throughout this organ, except for the main power supply and audio amplifier). Fig. 4-9 illustrates the Wien-bridge resistance-capacitance oscil-

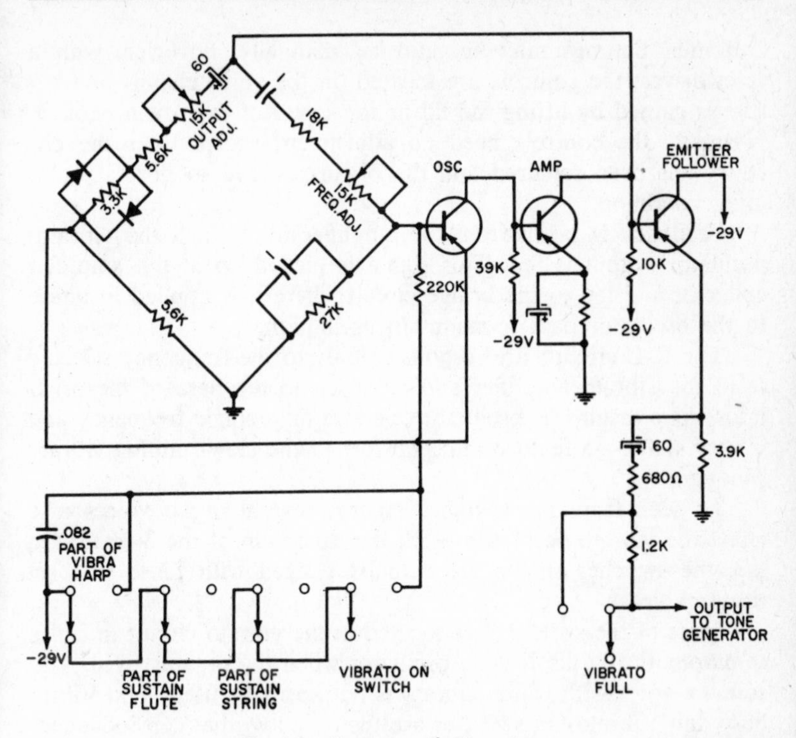

Fig. 4-9. Magnavox vibrato system.

lator, comparable to the phase-shift type. Frequency of oscillation is determined mainly by the R-C network time constants in the base circuit of the oscillator transistor.

Oscillator frequency may be controlled to some extent by the 15K potentiometer connected in the base circuit. This control alters the time constant enough to change the feedback frequency. Amplitude of the output signal may be varied by the 15K potentiometer connected in the emitter circuit of the oscillator. Both controls are preset by the manufacturer and are unavalible to the customer. Settings may be adjusted manually, however, with a screwdriver; the controls are located on the voice chassis and access is gained by lifting the lid or top cover of the organ cabinet. Normally the controls need no adjustment except after the circuitry has been repaired and the organ restored to normal operating condition.

Feedback is taken from the amplifier into which the vibrato-oscillator output is fed. This signal is picked up at the amplifier collector and fed to the bridge circuit where it is applied in phase to the oscillator base to maintain oscillation.

The R-C circuits are responsive only to the frequency selected from the vibrato amplifier and fed back to the base of the oscillator. As a result, the oscillator operates on a single frequency and is very stable—a feature indispensible to the slow-running vibrato generator.

As seen from the switches (tabs), several organ voices also affect the vibrato oscillator. With the exception of the Vibrato-On tab, the switches shown are actually ganged with those that set up the voices.

Some of the switches are located in the vibrato circuit in order to automatically disable the oscillator when the organist wishes to sound a voice with which vibrato is not normally used. The Vibraharp and Vibrato On switches are the only two that can independently turn on the –29 volts to actuate the oscillator. The vibraharp voice mixes the vibrato in automatically.

The output from the first vibrato amplifier is fed through an emitter-follower stage to provide an impedance match to the tone generators. The emitter-follower output is connected to the main base bias line and thereby sine-wave modulation is applied to all master oscillators within the main tone generating system. In turn, all of the Eccles-Jordan divider networks are modulated at the vibrato rate because of the coupling between the master oscillator and divider, and between each adjacent divider circuit.

HAMMOND

Model L-100

The Hammond Model L-100 organ utilizes a vibrato system entirely different from those previously discussed. It is not practical to modulate (as is done in many organs using electronic oscillators) the mechanical tone generators used by Hammond. A different approach must be taken to provide the vibrato effect.

The L-100 vibrato circuit (Fig. 4-10) uses a phase-shift vibrato oscillator to provide the reference frequency for the circuit. (This type of oscillator has been discussed previously and will not be enlarged upon again here—the discussion of this circuit will begin with the output signal from the vibrato oscillator.) The oscillator output is connected through a .1-mfd capacitor to two voltage-divider networks. Two values of amplitude are made available to the cathode-follower amplifier, which acts as a buffer stage for coupling the output load to the succeeding amplifier. Thus, isolation is maintained between vibrato oscillator and accompanying load.

The cathode follower is coupled to a triode amplifier with three series-connected saturable-reactor transformers in the plate circuit. The secondary windings are coupled to the plate and cathode circuits of three phase-shift stages. Output from the manual amplifier is fed into these phase-shift networks. In this way the vibrato effect may be applied to all organ tones.

A continuous phase shift may be accomplished by controlling, with reactor transformers, 180° out-of-phase signals from the plate and cathode of each phase shift stage. Each stage has identical plate and cathode resistors; as a result, signals are equal in amplitude in each plate and cathode circuit. The saturable reactors provide a varying composite of signals from both the plate and cathode of each stage, ranging from virtually full cathode to full plate signal.

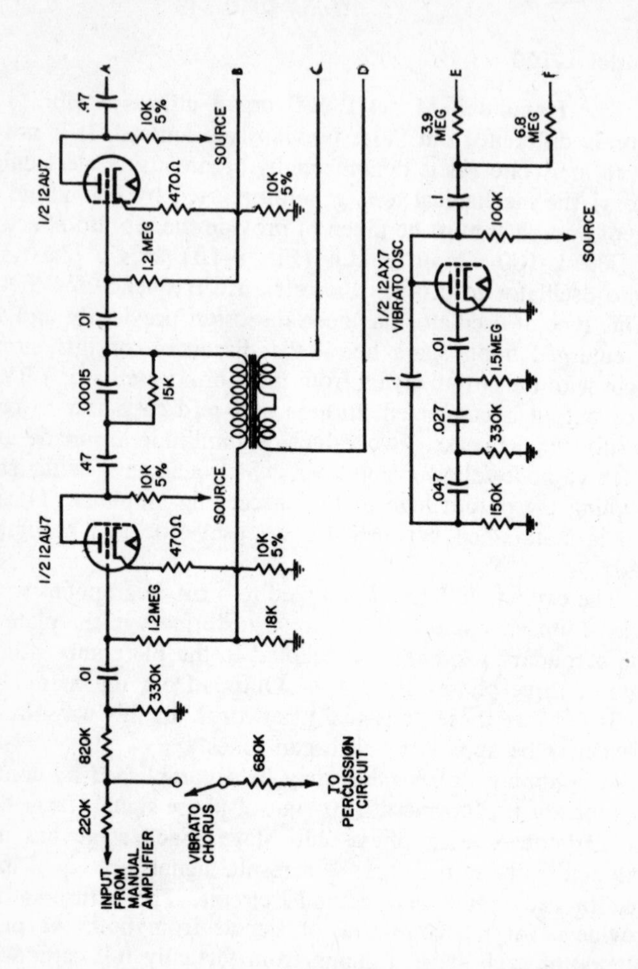

Fig. 4-10. Hammond vibrato

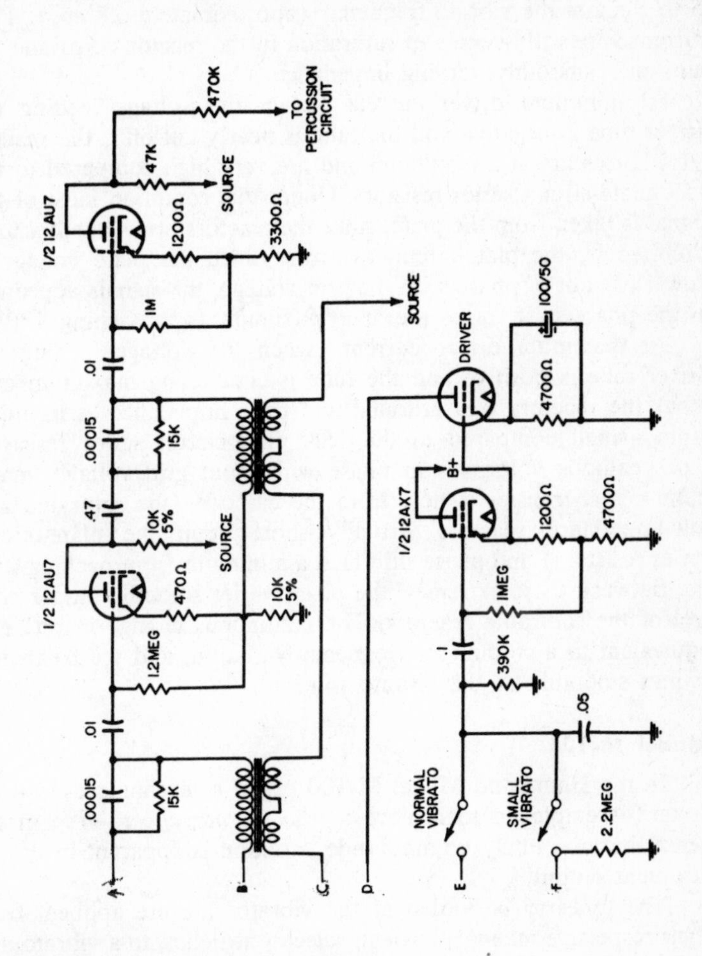

system (Model L-100).

The driver-tube plate current may be expected to vary from .5 to 5 ma at the vibrato frequency (approximately 6.8 cps). This current varies the degree of saturation in the reactor cores and results in a smoothly varying impedance.

At minimum driver current (when the voltage feeding the driver tube is negative and the tube is nearly cut off), the reactor impedances are at a maximum and are very high compared to the 15K plate-circuit series resistors. Under this condition most of the signal is taken from the plate, since the reactors are virtually short-circuited by the plate-circuit resistors. Since the plate voltage is now 180° out of phase with the grid voltage, the signals appearing in the phase-shift stages are at a maximum (approaching 180°).

At maximum driver current (when the voltage feeding the driver tube is positive and the tube is conducting maximum current) the reactors are saturated and their impedance at its minimum—small compared to the 15K plate-circuit series resistors. Since cathode voltage is in phase with input grid voltage, maximum signal transfer is now from the cathode (the saturated and low-impedance reactors virtually short-circuit the plate-circuit series resistors) and phase shift is at a minimum (approaching 0°).

Between these extremes, the phase varies smoothly under control of the saturable reactors. The continuous change in phase is equivalent to a continuous frequency variation, and the frequency swings smoothly at the vibrato rate.

Model M-100

In the Hammond Model M-100 organ a mechanical-electrical system is employed to achieve a *true vibrato effect*—true in the sense that absolutely no amplitude variation is apparent in the instrument output.

The tones to be varied at the vibrato rate are applied, from their respective manuals through selector switches, to a vibrato amplifier. A separate amplifier channel is selected by the Vibrato

Cancel tabs when vibrato is not desired. The vibrato amplifier and associated tab switches are illustrated in Fig. 4-11.

Signals from the manuals appear on the arm or center contact of the Vibrato Cancel switches. The setting of these switches, controlled by tabs on the organ control panel, determines whether the signal is passed to the vibrato or nonvibrato amplifier. The switches shown on the partial schematic are in the Vibrato On position.

Signals from the manuals are connected to the voltage amplifier. Cathode bias is obtained through the same 1200-ohm cathode

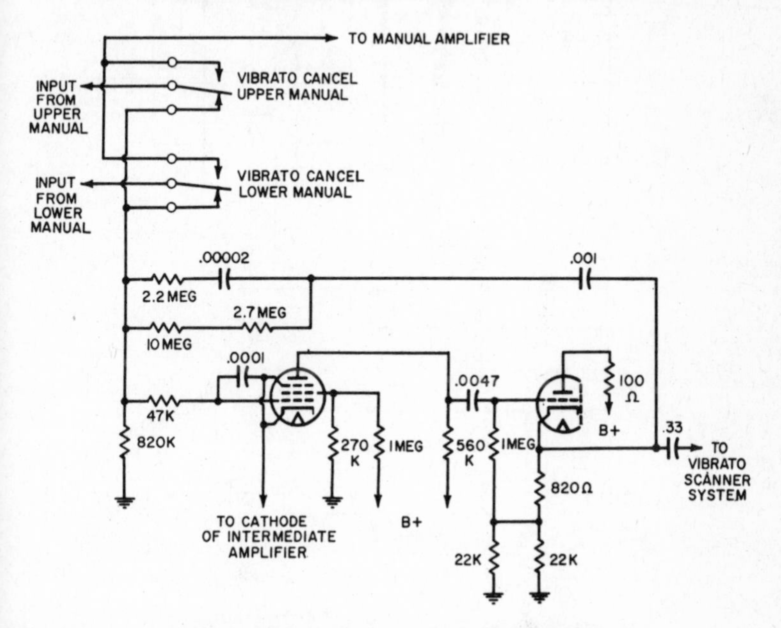

Fig. 4-11. Hammond vibrato circuit (Model M-100).

resistors connected to the intermediate-amplifier cathode. Output from this amplifier is capacitively coupled to the triode cathode-

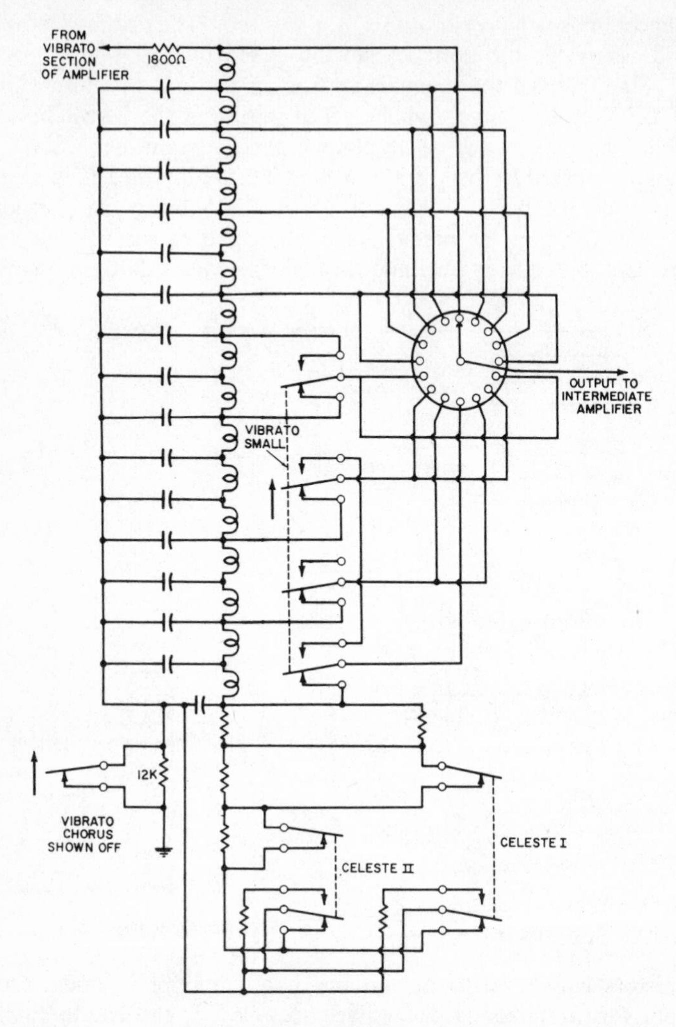

Fig. 4-12. Hammond vibrato delay line.

follower amplifier, which provides an impedance match to the vibrato-delay line (Fig. 4-12). A feedback network in the cathode, connected to the first vibrato amplifier input, helps flatten response.

The delay line and mechanical scanner used in the Hammond Model M-100 are illustrated in Fig. 4-12. This model uses an inductance, with a motor-driven scanning device, to provide a phase-shift modulation at the vibrato rate. The tones to be varied are connected directly across the inductance.

Notice the inductance is tapped at several points and connected to outside terminals of the mechanical scanner. Because of its inductance, signals present across the coil definitely lag at all tapped points, and the phase of any signal applied to the inductance varies accordingly at each point.

The center arm of the mechanical scanner is driven around the tap contacts, and the phase-shifted signal present at each tap is capacitively coupled to the intermediate amplifier. The scanner arm is driven by a synchronous motor at a constant rate of 412 revolutions per minute.

The output from the mechanical scanner consists of the same tones originally applied to the circuits; all signals, however, are now constantly varying in phase. The effect is the same as if these tones were being frequency modulated.

The amount of vibrato may be controlled to some extent by the Vibrato Small tab, which varies the amount of frequency shift by removing part of the inductive line from the scanning circuit. When the switch is in the Off position, as in Fig. 4-11, the entire line is being scanned.

A celeste effect is achieved by depressing either Vibrato Celeste I or Vibrato Celeste II, which in either case connects a resistor to the far end of the vibrato line, changing the termination impedance and producing reflected waves on the line. The reflected signal is passed by the scanner to the intermediate amplifier.

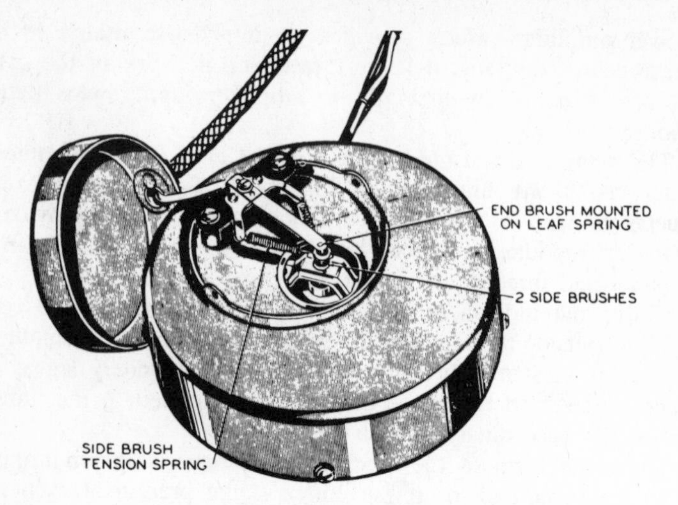

A-BRUSH COVER REMOVED TO SHOW BRUSHES

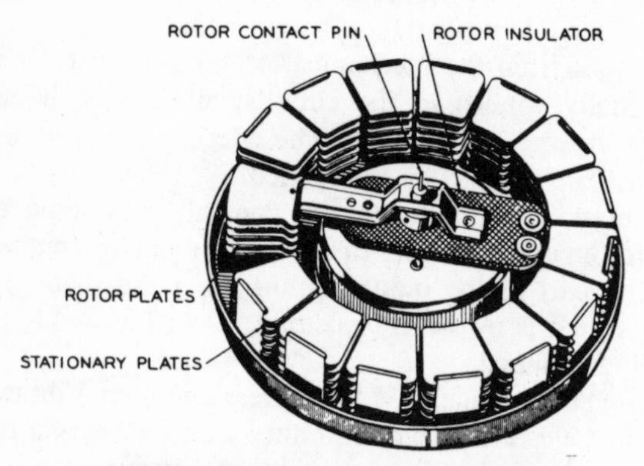

B-VIEW WITH SCANNER COVER REMOVED
(2 SETS OF PLATES REMOVED TO SHOW ROTOR)

Courtesy Hammond Organ Company.

Fig. 4-13. Hammond mechanical scanner assembly.

Vibrato chorus effect may be taken from the delay line by depressing the Vibrato Chorus tab, which causes the output to sound like a mixture of two or three frequencies slightly out of tune. With this tab down, only a portion of the incoming signal appears across the vibrato line, the remainder appearing across the resistor in series with the line. The former portion receives the vibrato effect while the latter is unaffected. A combination of the two on the output creates the chorus effect.

The physical structure of the mechanical scanner is shown in Fig. 4-13. It is a multi-pole variable capacitor with 16 sets of stationary plates meshing with the rotatable plates. Signals from the vibrato line appear on the stationary plates and are picked up, one at a time, by the rotor. Connection to the rotor is made by carbon brushes—two against the sides of the contact pin and a third pressed against the end to avoid contact failure and dead spots during rotation.

ALLEN

The Allen vibrato circuit is illustrated in Fig. 4-14. The vibrato oscillator is connected in a modified Hartley circuit, using a triode connected, 6L6 beam power pentode located on the power-supply chassis.

An iron-core inductance and associated components form the resonant circuit of the oscillator. The components are factory selected to derive the correct vibrato rate. The output from the vibrato generator is taken from one end of the inductance. From there it is then taken to switches where it may be turned on and fed to either the Solo- or Accompaniment-tone generator. Two amplitudes of vibrato modulation are available to the former.

Notice the Light Vibrato and Full Vibrato switches may be actuated by tabs on the front of the organ console. In the Full Vibrato position, output from the vibrato generator is connected

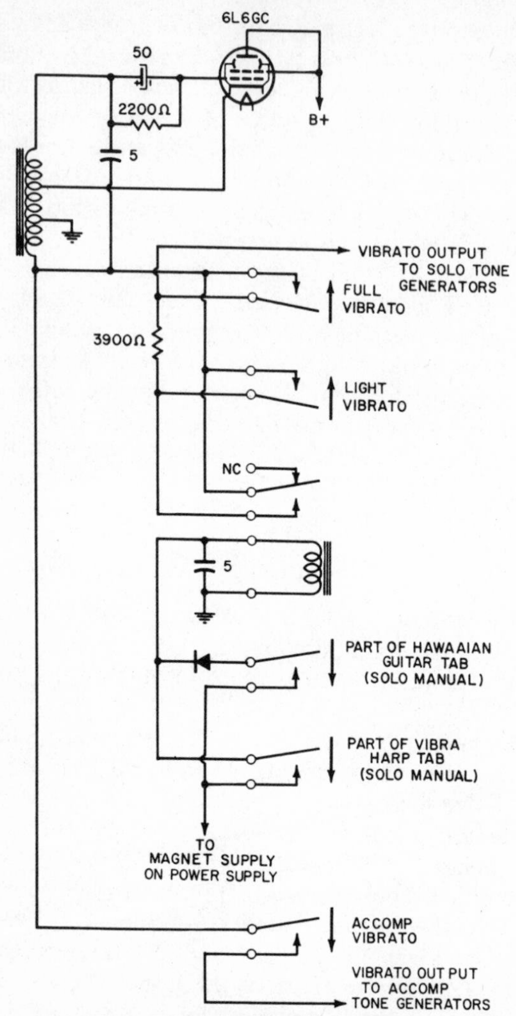

Fig. 4-14. Allen vibrato oscillator.

directly to the solo-tone generators. The Light Vibrato position connects a 3,900-ohm resistor in series with the vibrato output, to attenuate (somewhat) the signal fed to modulate the solo generators at the vibrato rate.

Only one level of vibrato is available to the accompaniment tone generators. Notice that the Accompaniment Vibrato tab is connected directly to the vibrato-generator output. The only purpose of this switch is to furnish vibrato to the accompaniment-tone generators.

Two other tabs, Hawaiian Guitar and Vibra Harp, also automatically turn on the light vibrato to the solo-tone generators. Depressing either tab turns on a voltage source to a relay coil. The contacts of this relay are pulled together giving the same effect as if the Light Vibrato tab were depressed. (Note: The Hawaiian Guitar and Vibra Harp tabs represent only a portion of the switch. Other functions also take place when these tabs are actuated.)

KINSMAN

Another organ which employs a phase-shift type oscillator for the vibrato generator is the Kinsman. The circuit shown in Fig. 4-15 is representative for all Kinsman models except Model D, which will be discussed separately.

All Models Except D

The Kinsman phase-shift oscillator is essentially the same as the others discussed except for the feedback take-off point. In the Kinsman, feedback for sustaining vibrato oscillation is picked up at the cathode. The oscillator is stabilized to some extent by the 8-megohm resistor connected from the tube plate to the grid. No coupling is obtained at this point because the plate is effectively at ground potential as far as the signal is concerned.

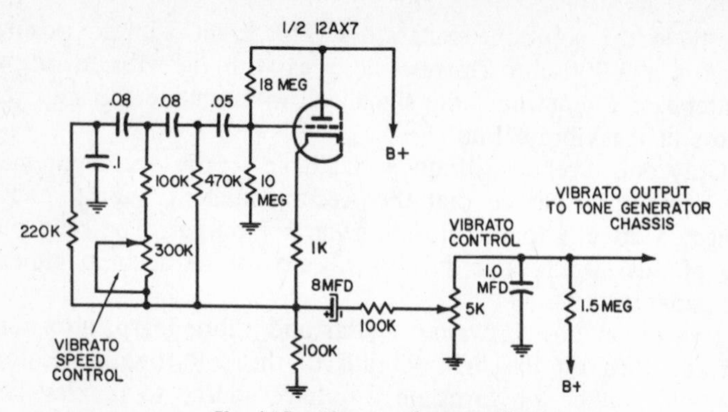

Fig. 4-15. Kinsman vibrato oscillator.

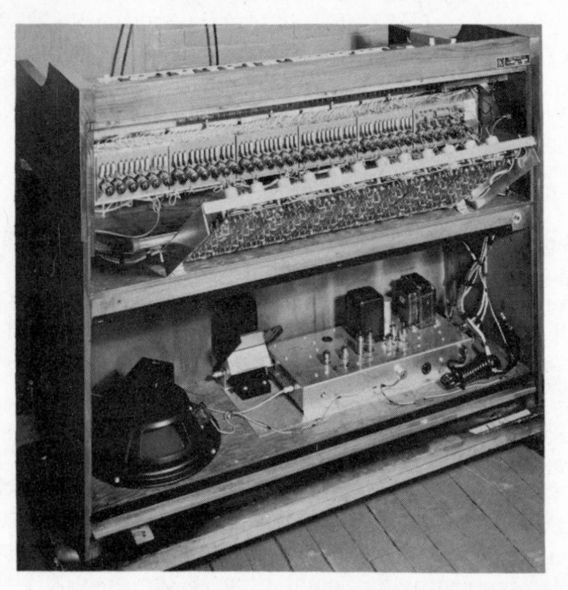

Courtesy Kinsman Manufacturing Co., Inc.

Fig. 4-16. Rear view of Kinsman organ.

The frequency rate of the vibrato signal may be altered slightly by rotating the Vibrato-Speed control, which changes the R-C time constant of the grid circuit and establishes a new operating point for the vibrato oscillator.

The amount of vibrato may be controlled by the Vibrato-Output control, which determines vibrato-signal amplitude fed to the tone generators for modulation. By rotating this control counterclockwise, the vibrato output is shorted to ground and no vibrato signal appears at the tone generators.

The vibrato output signal is fed to all master oscillators in the tone-generator assembly. As it is being applied, the 1.5-megohm resistor at the vibrato output (common to all master-oscillator grid circuits in the main generator assembly) places all grid circuits under identical loading. The vibrato oscillator tube, a 12AX7, and its associated controls are located on the amplifier and power-supply chassis (Fig. 4-16).

Model D

The Model D vibrato circuit is unique among Kinsman models. It is similar in operation to the Hammond Model L-100. In Model D the familiar phase-shift oscillator is used to produce the vibrato rate. Oscillator frequency may be controlled from approximately 5.7 to 6.8 cps.

The Model D Great and Swell manuals may be operated two ways: together with both giving the vibrato effect; or individually, one giving the vibrato and the other the normal effect. This advantage, of course, gives Model D added versatility.

The vibrato oscillator and associated circuitry are illustrated in Fig. 4-17. It can be seen that each manual output is connected to an impedance-matching amplifier which raises the level of the manual signals and incorporates an impedance match from the manuals to the first amplifier.

When the Swell and Great vibrato switches are in the Off position (as illustrated), the manual signals bypass the vibrato cir-

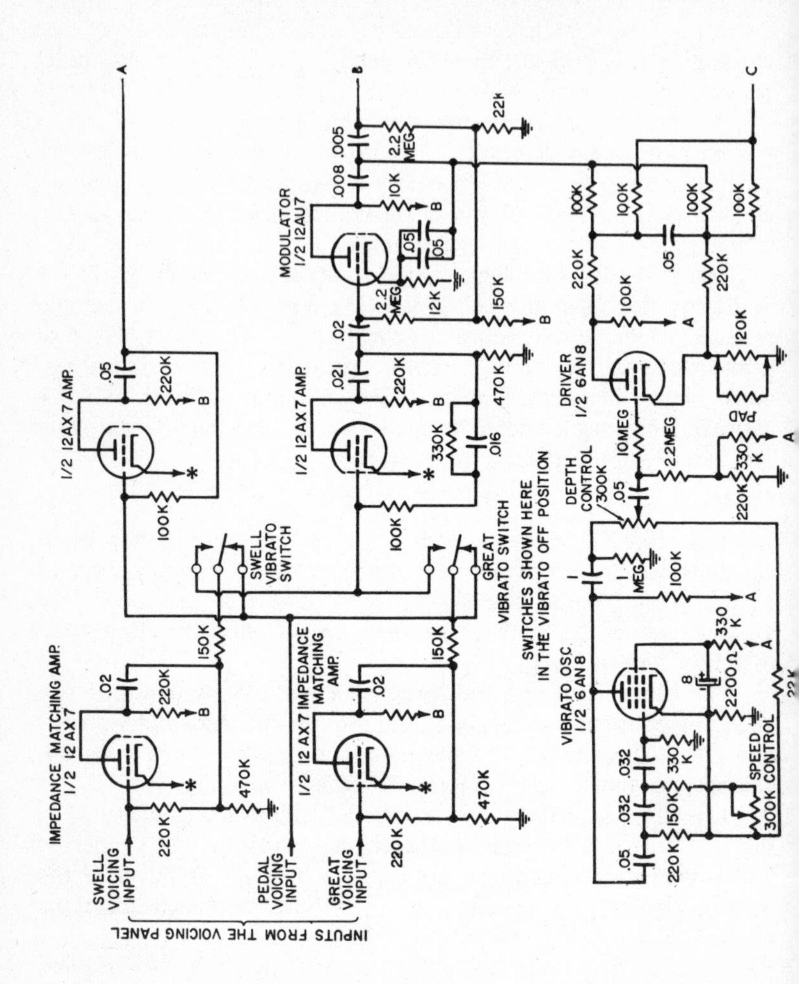

Fig. 4-17. Kinsman

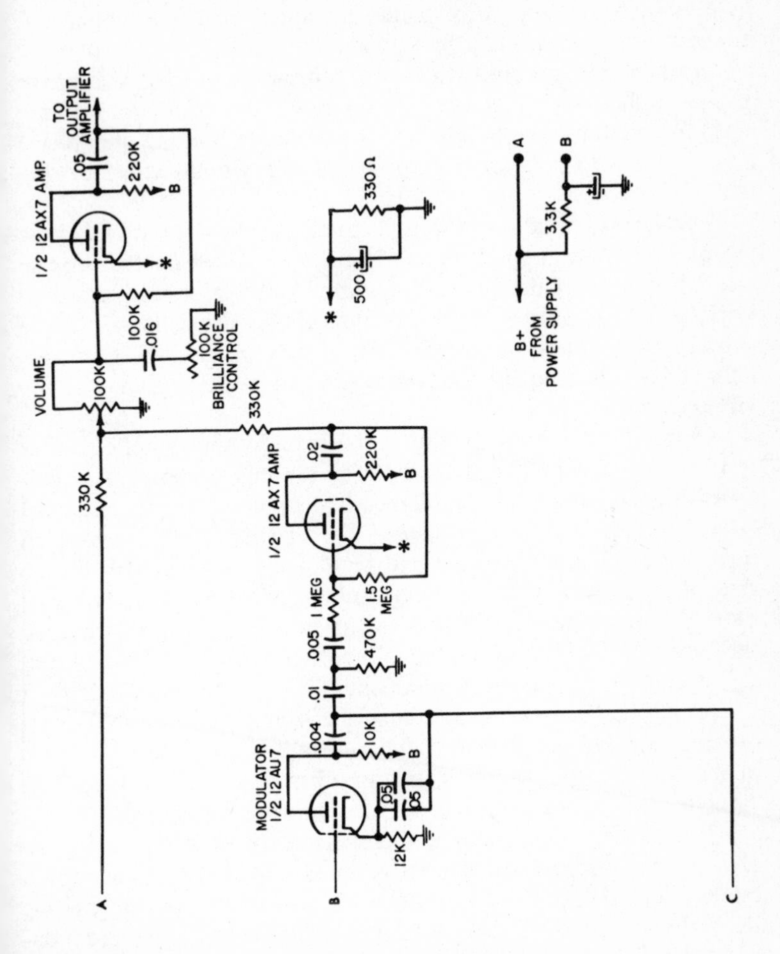

vibrato system.

cuitry and no vibrato is applied to the manual tones. Depress either switch and the corresponding manual output is connected to the vibrato channel. The signal then passes through two vibrato-modulator circuits which are constantly shifting the phase of the applied signal at the vibrato rate. The continuous phase
brato-modulator circuits which are constantly shifting the phase
highly satisfactory means for producing the vibrato effect on the output.

Further examination of the schematic in Fig. 4-17 reveals how the phase of the applied manual signals is shifted at the vibrato rate. Output from the phase-shift vibrato oscillator is coupled to a triode balanced driver. The function of this driver is to provide two signals of equal amplitude, 180° apart, to the vibrato-modulator tubes. The frequency of these two out-of-phase signals is the vibrato rate.

Output from the driver tube is balanced by the cathode padder resistor, selected by the manufacturer for this purpose. The balanced signal is applied simultaneously to the cathode and grid circuits of the vibrato modulator. The applied vibrato signal, in turn, varies the cathode and grid bias of the tubes at the vibrato rate of frequency. Since each modulator tube receives its signal 180° out of phase with respect to the other, signals pass through the tubes by way of either the cathode or the plate. This output signal continually varies in phase by 180° at the vibrato rate.

It may be seen from this that the vibrato driver-tube signal controls the biasing of the modulator tubes, and thereby determines whether the output signal is taken from the plate or the cathode before being passed to the following amplifier.

The Model D oscillator is independent of other circuitry, except for establishing the reference signal which biases the modulator. Oscillator-frequency rate may be altered slightly by rotating the Vibrato Speed control, available to the organist on the stop-action assembly.

In other Kinsman models, the vibrato assembly is an integral part of the main amplifier chassis; in Model D it is located on a separate printed board.

CHAPTER 5

Keyswitches

The keyswitch is the device actuated to select the desired note on an electronic organ. In general, these switches fall into two categories: *manuals,* (solo and accompaniment) played with the hands; and the *pedals,* played with the feet.

Although the keyswitches used in modern electronic organs vary widely in structure, they all have a common function: to make electrical contact between two or more points. This primary contact sets into motion the pattern of events which leads to the sounding of the organ tone. Although often involving several actions, the sequence is easily understood in each organ model here discussed by analyzing one switch and putting it visually through its paces.

For each model considered, the keyswitch is diagramed to show its mechanical arrangement and the manner in which it is electrically connected into the circuit. Since this book assumes that the service technician is capable of analyzing most of the electrical connections on his own, the stress here is on physical characteristics of each keyswitch.

HAMMOND

The keyswitches employed in the Hammond Models L-100 and M-100 are shown in Fig. 5-1. A single keyswitch and its associated contacts are shown as viewed directly from the side of the keyswitch manual assembly.

To fully understand the action, it is necessary to follow a key through the entire cycle. For the sake of explanation, assume the key shown is Middle *C* on the lower manual of the organ. Nine contacts actuated by the key, make with nine corresponding bus lines which run the entire length of the manual keyswitch assembly. Each switch contact is wired to a tone generator through a length of wire having a resistance of 16 ohms.

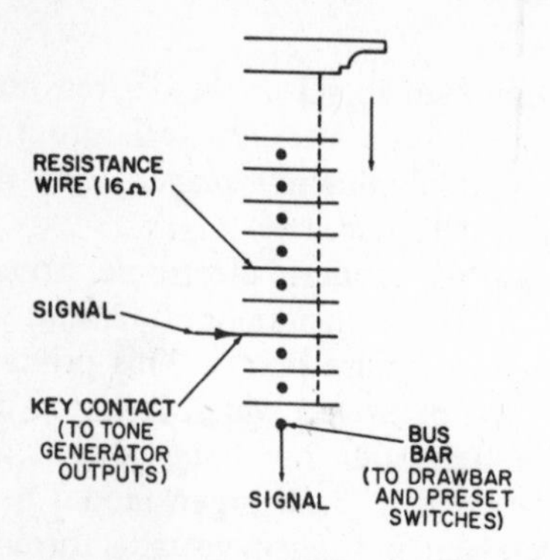

Fig. 5-1. Hammond L-100 and M-100 keyswitch.

The tone generators, connected to the contacts, in the case of Middle *C,* are numbers 37, 49, 56, 61, 65, 68, 73, 77, and 80. These numbers refer to the tone-generator sequence, which runs from the lowest generator frequency (number 1 on the pedalboard) to the highest tone on the manual keyboard (approximately 91 in the Hammond models). The numbers are needed to show the relationship between voice tabs, tone generators, and keyswitch contacts.

The generator outputs are present at the bus lines when the key is depressed. The signals may then be passed on either with the preset tabs or the drawbars. (The harmonic drawbars and preset tab action are discussed in Chapter 8.)

There are three preset tabs on the lower manual, labeled Flute, Diapason, and Ensemble. To produce one of these voices the tab is depressed, actuating an eight-contact switch. Fundamental and harmonic signals at the keyswitch bus lines are combined and passed through the preset tab switch. Since all voice simulation in these Hammond models is accomplished in the same manner (i.e., by the mixture of harmonics) the explanation of flute voice simulation will serve as an example for the others.

When the Flute tab (Fig. 5-2) is depressed, outputs from generators 37, 49, 61, and 73 are combined and fed to a tap on a matching coupling transformer. At the same time, outputs from 56, 65, 68, 77, and 80 are grounded.

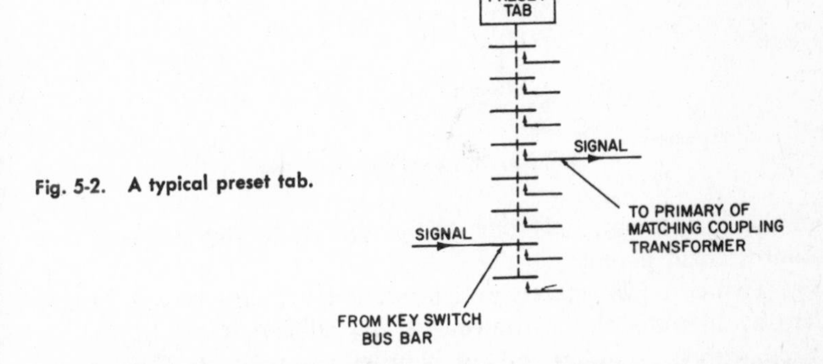

Fig. 5-2. A typical preset tab.

The drawbars, when used, receive a signal through the drawbar tab. The construction of this tab is basically the same as that of the preset tab; its function is to channel the signal from the keyswitch bus bars to the drawbars. All phases of the note played are then related to the drawbar to which it is connected. As this bar is pulled out or pushed in, the intensity of the signal is changed and the tone color may be controlled accordingly. Fig. 5-3 shows the mechanical make-up of this system. Because of the design

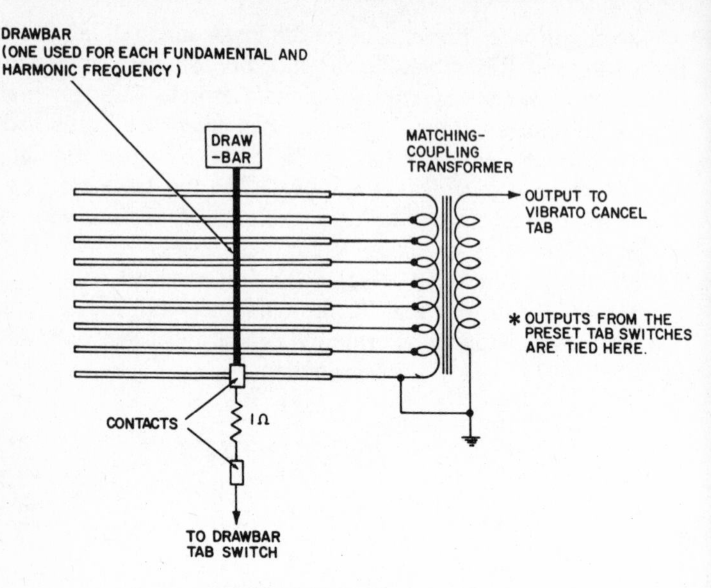

Fig. 5-3. A typical drawbar system.

of the instrument, only one of the four tabs mentioned may be depressed at a time.

Two contacts, spaced so that one is touching a bus at all times (to avoid nulls as the drawbar is passed across the buses), are used with a 100-ohm resistor between the contacts. The resistor prevents shorting of adjacent buses.

CONN

Several keyswitch assemblies utilize the *coupler rod,* a type of busbar which is rather heavy and extends the length of the keyboard assembly. In this system, when a key is depressed, the keyswitch contacts make with the rods. In some cases the coupler rods

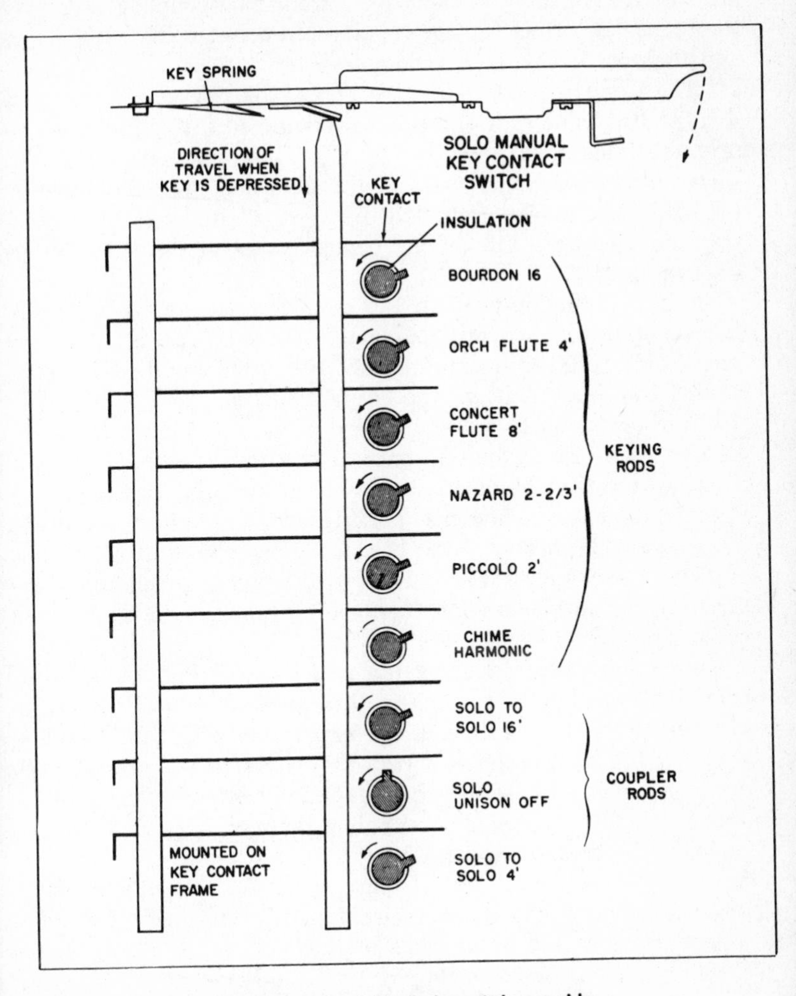

Fig. 5-4. Conn 540 solo keyswitch assembly.

are rotatable, making possible the intramanual coupling necessary to obtain the correct footage relationship between the keyswitches and their respective tone generators.

The Conn Models 540 and 625 employ the coupler rod system. At least nine rods are used to provide all the coupling necessary from the tone generator to the output amplifier. Fig. 5-4 shows a cross-sectional view of the keyswitch assembly used in the solo manual. The rods used here are all rotatable by depressing the associated tab on the control panel at the front of the organ console.

In the Conn Model 625, the coupler rods are mechanically connected to their corresponding tabs by small cables. *Extreme care* should be taken when lifting the top of the console—the connecting cables are delicate and easily damaged.

The key contacts are small bare wires set in plastic dowels. Depressing a key on the solo manual keyboard forces all the contacts downward simultaneously. Each coupler rod has a projection, or ridge, extending the length of the rod, which comprises the conducting portion of the bus line. Each rod is plated with a precious metal to insure total keyswitch contact; and each, except for the projection and contact portions, is insulated with plastic.

When their corresponding tab is depressed, the coupler rods rotate approximately one-quarter turn so their projections are in position to make contact with the key contact wires. In Fig. 5-4, the direction of rotation is shown by arrows to the side of each of the coupler rods. Each rod couples the output voice to the voicing circuits. Intramanual coupling between key contacts then provides the different footage lengths.

The key contacts in these Conn organs are, as a rule, mechanically trouble-free; occasional cleaning helps to keep them that way. If noise should occur when a keyswitch is depressed, always check to make certain the coupler rods and key contacts are clean and capable of making firm contact.

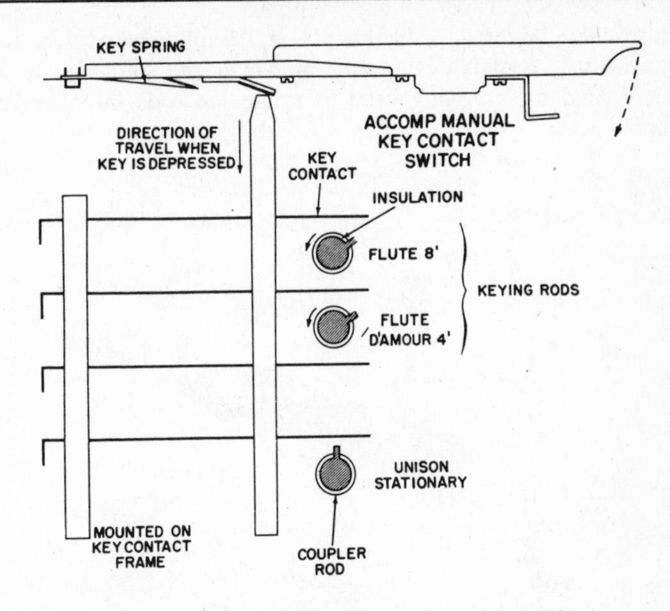

Fig. 5-5. Conn 540 accompaniment keyswitch assembly.

The keyswitch assembly used in the accompaniment manual of Conn Model 540 is essentially the same as that used in the solo manual. The only basic differences are in the number of key contacts per keyswitch, and the number of coupler rods (three rather than nine). A cross-section view of the accompaniment keyswitch assembly is pictured in Fig. 5-5. For a view of a key, see Fig. 5-6.

WURLITZER

The Wurlitzer 4100 Series organs also use a rotating coupler-rod system for conveying the signal from the tone generators to the main amplifier. It functions in much the same manner as the

Conn system. Differences lie mainly in the physical structure of the keyswitch assembly, the way in which the keyswitches are actuated, and the coupling used to rotate the rods into conducting position.

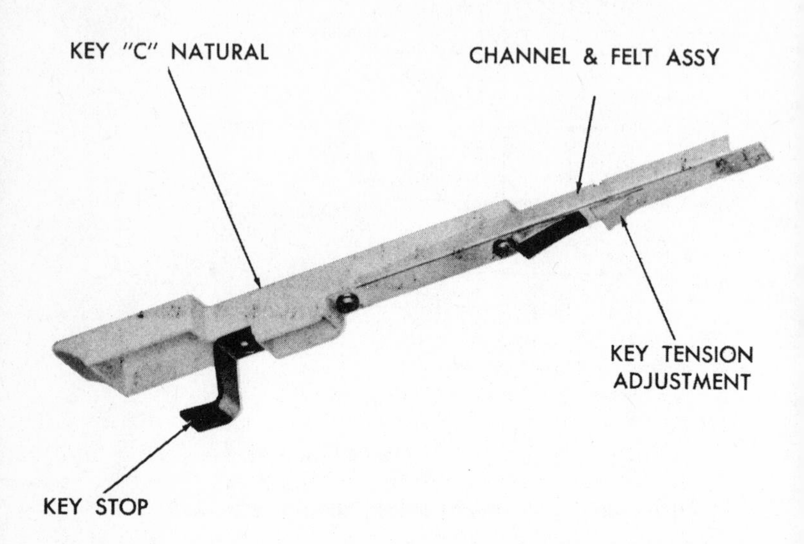

Fig. 5-6. A Conn key.

Fig. 5-7 shows the keyswitch and tab arrangement used in Model 4100. The coupler rods in this model are constructed of glass with a conductive ridge extending the entire length of the rod. All connections are similar to that shown in the illustration. The complete signal path may be followed from the tone generator, through the keyswitch assembly and tab switch, to the main amplifier.

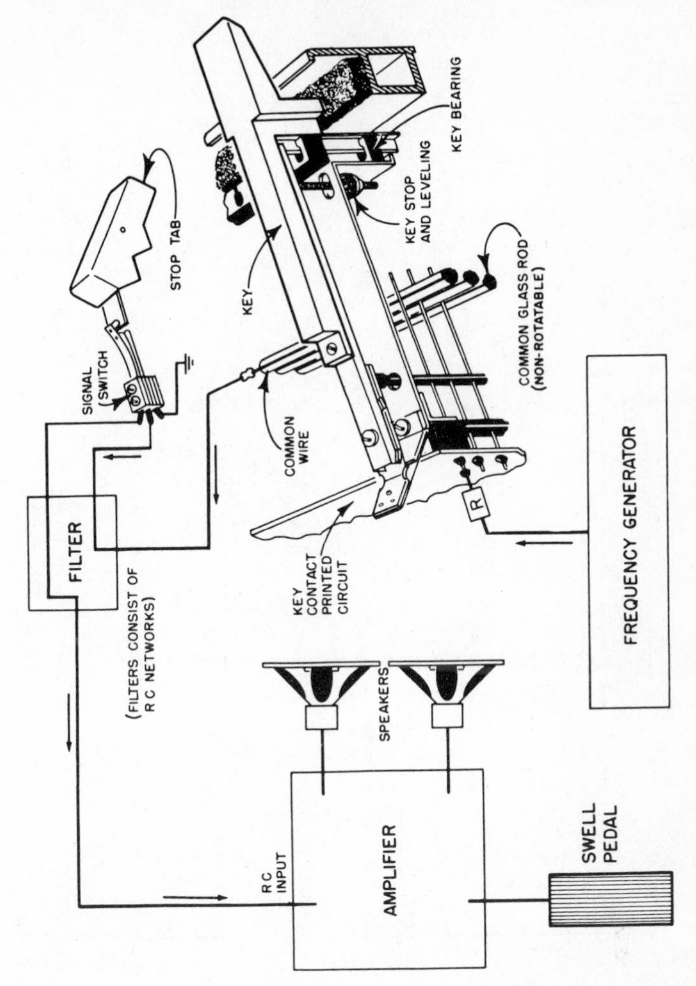

Courtesy Wurlitzer Company.

Fig. 5-7. Wurlitzer 4100 keyswitch and tab arrangement.

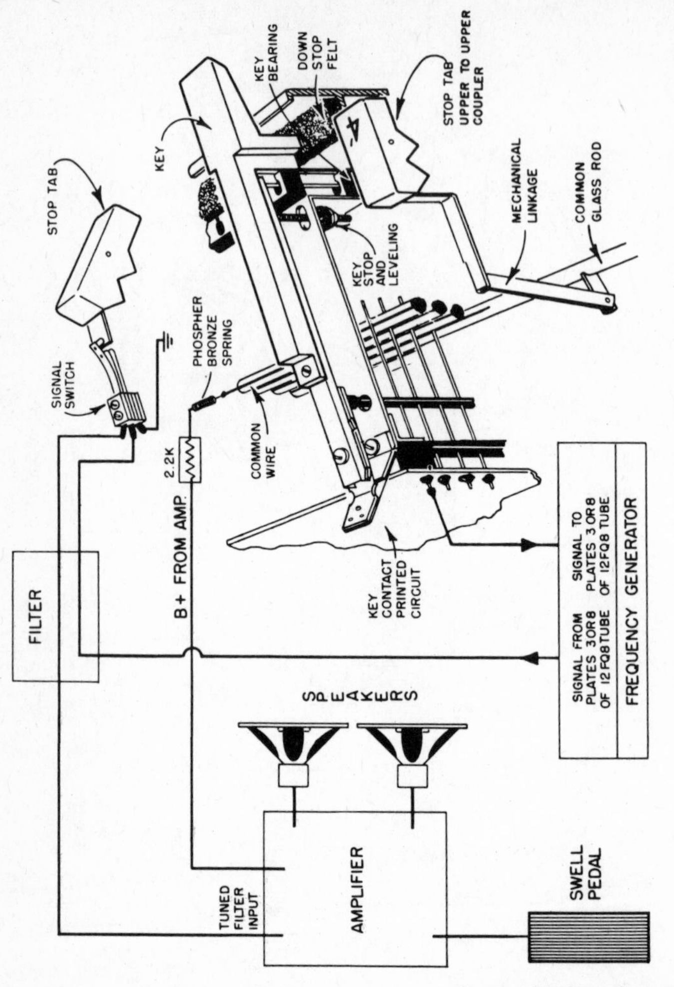

Courtesy Wurlitzer Company.

Fig. 5-8. A typical Wurlitzer rod and linkage.

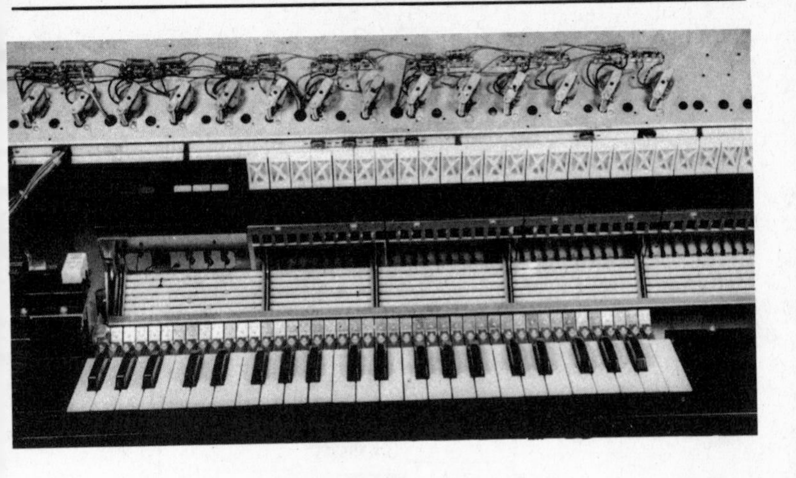

Fig. 5-9. Wurlitzer 4100 keyswitch assembly.

The leads are connected through springs to make the coupling flexible and prevent breakage as the rods are rotated. A typical rod for the Wurlitzer keyboard assembly is shown in Fig. 5-8, along with the mechanical linkage that couples to cause rotation of the rod. The rest of the assembly is much the same as the one shown in Fig. 5-7. The coupling from the tone generator through the keyswitch contact is in the physical position, to represent the percussible keying circuit.

Fig. 5-9 shows the Wurlitzer Model 4100 keyswitch assembly as it appears with the solo manual lifted. The coupler rods are clearly visible.

MAGNAVOX

The keyswitch assembly of the Magnavox Model A-10 is designed to give automatic partial control of the tone attack. (The term "attack" designates the time required for the tone to reach its full intensity after depressing the key.)

The keyswitch lines are covered with conductive rubber composition. The bus lines are bare wire sleeved over with the same material (which makes them appear to be solidly encased in insulation). The entire arrangement is illustrated in Fig. 5-10.

The key contacts consist of small bare wires, set into a printed board arrangement, with insulation slid over a portion of their surface to help maintain sturdy contact. The unit shown in Fig. 5-10 is representative of all the keyswitch contacts and bus lines (four of each are contained in the solo manual and two of each in the accompaniment manual).

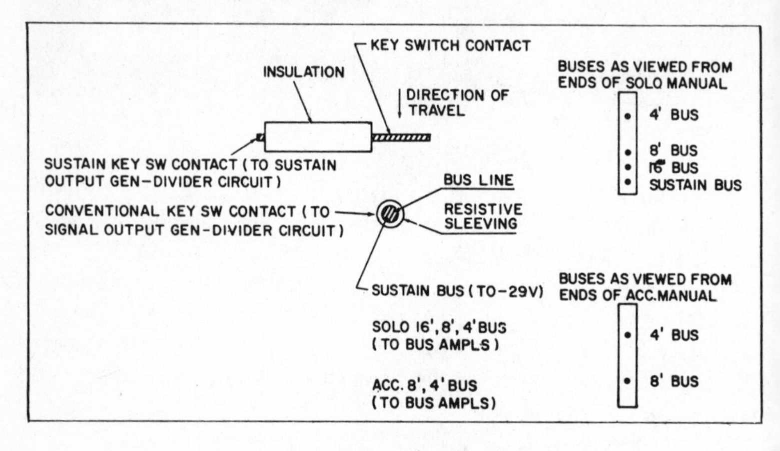

Fig. 5-10. Magnavox A-10 bus line.

When a keyswitch is depressed in the solo manual four key-contact switches are actuated simultaneously, and one bus line becomes connected into the voicing circuits. In the accompaniment manual the same thing occurs, except only two key contact switches are actuated.

As the key contact makes with the resistive sleeving over the bus lines, resistance remains high until the key is firmly depressed.

The tone is then allowed to pass from the tone generator; the tone generator circuit however, is not keyed instantaneously, but slowly giving control and preventing the tone from sounding with an explosive attack. To increase the attack of the tone, it is only necessary to depress the key quickly.

In the Magnavox, the signal does not pass through the keyswitches during a sustain condition. Instead, the keyswitches turn on a voltage to a corresponding diode gate circuit in the tone-generator assembly. The –29 volts applied to the sustain bus line permits attack control to be maintained. By connecting in this manner, keying voltage to the diode gate circuits is applied at a gradual rate, causing a slow reaction.

BALDWIN

The Baldwin Model 71-P keyswitches are much the same as those employed in Magnavox Model A-10. Differences, of course, are found in mechanical construction of the keyswitch assembly.

Fig. 5-11 shows a typical Baldwin 71-P keyswitch arrange-

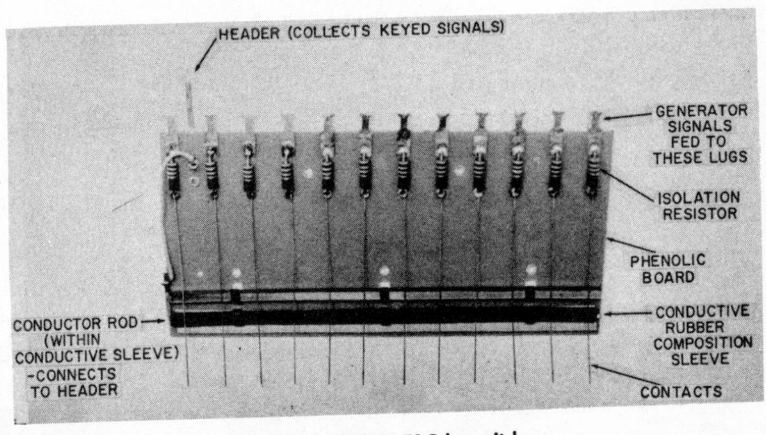

Fig. 5-11. Baldwin 71-P keyswitch.

ment; here one octave of keyswitches with isolation resistors is mounted on a circuit board. The header shown is the collecting line for all signals after they have been keyed.

The conductive rubber composition not only helps to control the attack of the tone, but attenuates the key clicks and transient effects as well. These characteristics are common in some models which employ direct contacts. In some cases a filter arrangement is employed in the direct contact keyswitches—especially where voltage is interrupted when the switch is actuated.

THOMAS

The keyswitch contact arrangement used in the Thomas Model V-1 (Fig. 5-12) is shown in Fig. 5-13. Mechanically these contacts are very similar to the others discussed; the bus line arrangement is different however. The keyswitch contacts make with a bus line in both the On and Off positions.

In this model, proper adjustment must be made with respect to the key contacts and their associated bus lines. If the contacts do not connect with the off bus lines in their normal resting position, notes may feed through even when no key is depressed on either manual.

Solo Manual Contact Adjustment

The solo manual key contacts may best be tested for adjustment and operation by separately playing each of the four flute-voice keys on the manual. Ideally the note should sound when the key is depressed between 30% and 60% (⅛ and ¼ inch at tip of white keys) of its total travel. The signal buses are arranged in order of increasing footage, with the 4′ bus at the top of the key coupler switch. When the 4′ stop is depressed, the uppermost row of contacts are involved. After completing the 4′ row adjustment, the 5⅓′ stop may be depressed, all keys played again, and the contact in the next row adjusted. This procedure is repeated

Courtesy Thomas Organ Company.

Fig. 5-12. Thomas "Serenade".

for the 8′ and 16′ contacts, each time dropping down a row to make the adjustment.

Adjustment of individual contacts may be made by tilting the resistor at the end of each contact either up or down. This causes the contact tip to move in the opposite direction. When all contacts are adjusted properly and the keys are at rest, there should be a relatively uniform spacing of approximately 3/16 (.188) inch between all contacts and their respective signal buses (Figure 5-13A). Occasionally, the contacts for a given key become *uniformly* spaced too far or too close to their respective buses. In such an event it is best to make the adjustment by bending up or down, as required, the ductile lifter pin which exits from the rear of the associated key. This same adjustment may be made to set the lowest row of percussion contacts. These should normally have a slight bow and rest firmly on the lower percussion busbar,

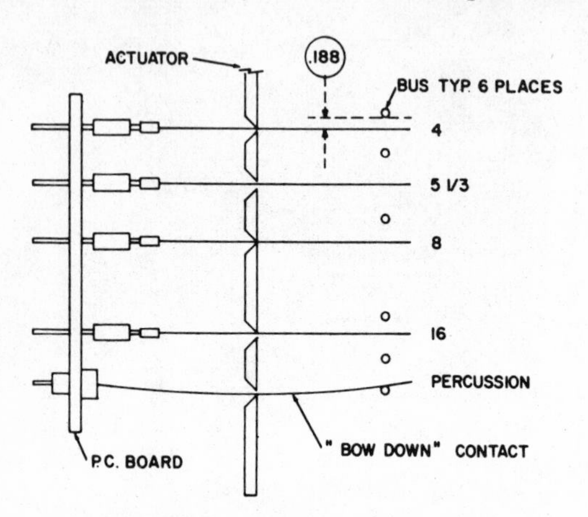

(A) Solo contact adjustment.

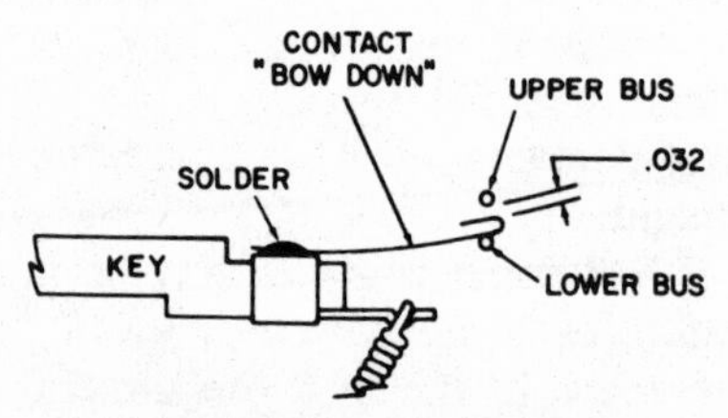

(B) Lower keyboard adjustment.

Fig. 5-13. Thomas V-1 keyswitch.

clearing it at approximately 60% of key travel and making contact with the upper percussion busbar at no more than 85% (approximately 5/16 inch at the tip of the white keys).

Adjustment of the lowest seven solo key contacts is made by starting with the percussion contact adjustment, as outlined above. Contact timing should also be the same as above except for the switch wires connecting with the crossed staples. These should be in a severe bowed-up condition when the key is at rest and should break from at least one of the crossed staples before the next higher contact makes to the horizontal staple directly above.

Lower Keyboard Switches

It is essential that, when the keys are at rest, the accompaniment or lower keyboard switch whiskers make with the associated grounding bus. If contact is not made, a small amount of 16′ tone will contaminate the solo manual voices.

When using the solo 8′ flute voice, contamination takes place an octave higher than the key on the accompaniment manual whose contact is not grounding. This condition may be simulated by insulating a contact from the grounding bus with a small piece of paper (or very slightly depressing the accompaniment key) while holding down the solo key an octave higher. By experimenting in this manner one can soon learn to recognize the contaminated sound. Whenever it is heard on the upper manual, improper lower manual grounding should be suspected immediately.

The contact may be best adjusted by applying a light upward or downward pressure to the whisker at the point where it leaves the soldered area at the rear of the key (Fig. 5-13B). The key should be depressed while bending the contact downward. Care must be taken to use the minimum wipe necessary to guarantee contact against the lower bus, so that adequate pressure is obtained when the key is depressed and the whisker contacts the upper bus.

CHAPTER 6

Percussion

Percussion has long been associated with music and musical instruments, but has become so varied in use that it is often confused with other musical effects. The term percussion is used rather loosely as applied in some of the electronic organs now in production. Occasionally it is used synonymously with the term sustain; however, this is not percussion in the true sense of the word.

Percussion is the effect produced by the forcible striking of one body against another. Percussion instruments (e.g. drums, xylophone, and piano) are those in which the vibrating system is excited by some manner of striking. In the organs considered here, percussion is simulated electronically.

HAMMOND

Model L-100

The Hammond L-100 organ offers a percussive output through the selection of appropriate tabs on the front of the console. The percussion circuitry for this organ is shown in Fig. 6-1.

The signal for the percussion amplifier is taken from either the second or third harmonic drawbar or both, depending on the tab selection. An upper manual is shown in Fig. 6-1 to illustrate

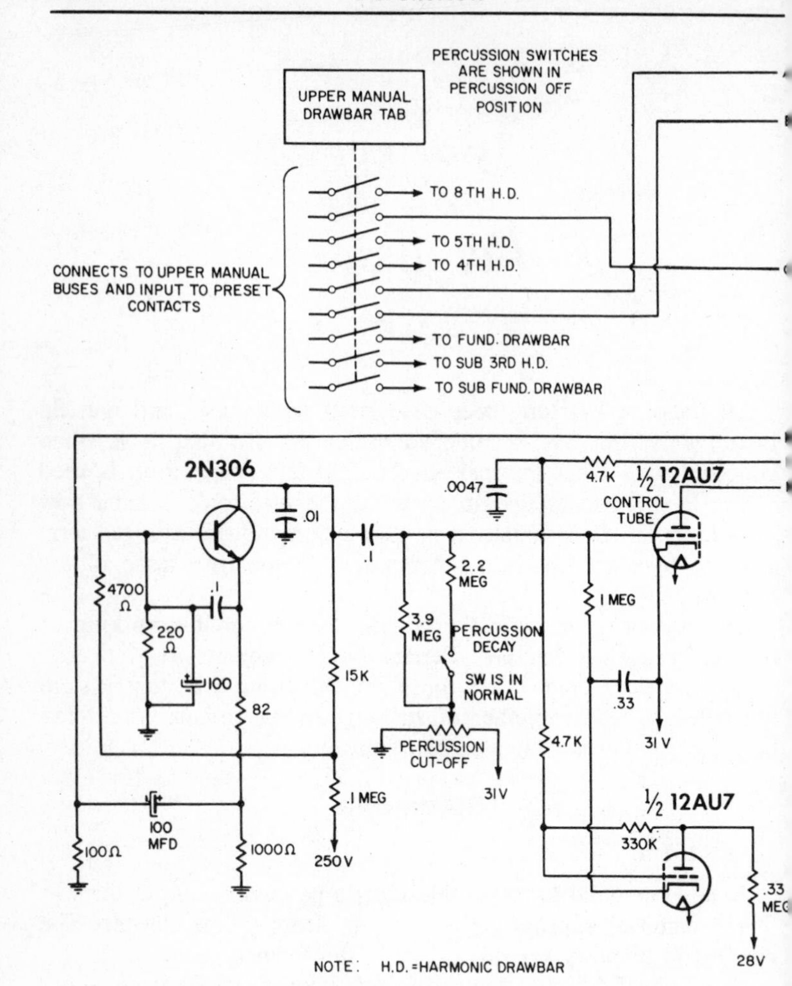

Fig. 6-1. Hammon

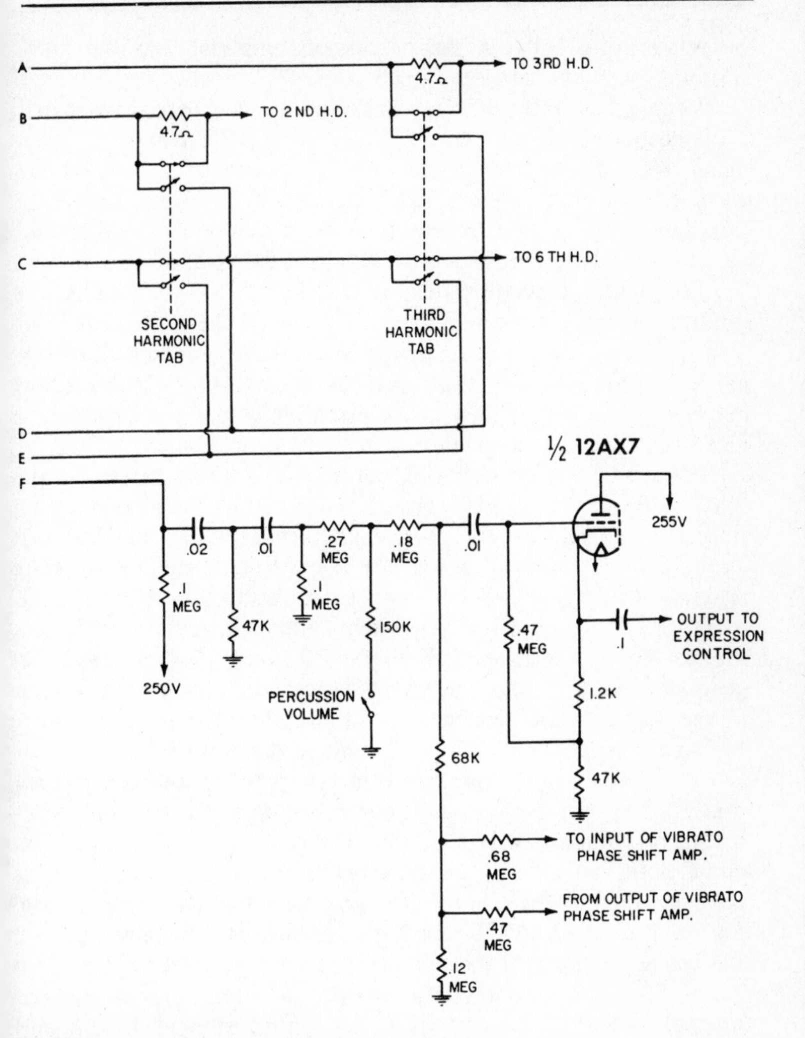

L-100 percussion system.

the relationship between the percussion amplifier and the take-off point for the percussion signal.

When either Harmonic tab is depressed, the percussive signal is connected to the emitter of the 2N306 NPN transistor. This signal, representing the second or third harmonic present on the upper manual, is then coupled to one-half of the triode (12AU7) amplifier. This section of the tube is normally conducting and functions as the control tube for the percussion condition.

The output from this tube is coupled to a cathode-follower amplifier which takes the percussion signal to the expression control; from there it is passed to the main audio amplifier. The signal will audibly differ from that of normal playing conditions because of the action that takes place when the percussion tabs are actuated and a keyswitch is depressed.

Percussion circuit action is controlled to some extent by the other half of the 12AU7 (which is actually diode-connected), since a resistance of only 330K exists between the plate and grid circuit. When either drawbar tab is depressed, the keying wire normally held at +28 volts is connected to the solo manual sixth-harmonic drawbar. As a keyswitch on the manual is depressed, the keying line is grounded through the key contact and tone-generator filter circuit. This effectively grounds the grid and plate of the 12AU7 diode-connected section. The tube is then reverse biased and appears as an open circuit to the control tube.

The control-tube grid then drifts from its operating potential, preset by the percussion cutoff control at 25 volts, to a cutoff potential of approximately 15 volts. The time required to reach the cutoff point depends on the time required for the .33-mfd capacitor connected to the control-tube grid circuit to discharge through the 3.9-megohm and 2.2-megohm grid resistors. The latter is not in the active circuit until the percussion Fast Decay tab is depressed.

No percussion notes will sound again until all of the solo manual keys are released and the control-tube grid voltage is allowed to rise to +25 volts. The recovery time of the control tube will also depend on the charging time constant of the .33-mfd capacitor.

The Percussion Volume tab reduces volume by shunting a 150K resistor into the divider network of the cathode-follower grid circuit.

A slight sustain signal may be attained simultaneous to the percussion effect, by inserting the 4.7-ohm resistor in series between the manual bus wire and the drawbars.

Model M-100

The Hammond M-100 also provides a percussion output. Its effects are similar to those obtained from the L-100; the circuitry (Fig. 6-2), however, is somewhat different.

Like the L-100, this model removes percussible signals from the second- and third-harmonic drawbars; in place of the transistor impedance-matching network, however, a percussion-matching transformer is used as the signal coupling device. Because of resistive feedback in the secondary winding, the primary resistance of this transformer is approximately 5 ohms. In this way primary loading is kept at a minimum so that, whether played singly or simultaneously, all notes have equal amplitude.

The impedance-matching transformer also couples the percussion signal to the first percussion amplifier. From this stage it is connected to a transformer providing a single plate to push-pull grid coupling. The push-pull triodes act as control tubes for the percussive signal. Another winding, of the coupling transformer, feeds the signal to the second- or third-harmonic drawbar through appropriate key-circuit resistors.

When a key is depressed and the second- or third-harmonic percussion first sounds loudly, the control tubes are in a normal conducting condition. The signal passes through the tube; to the output transformer; to a band pass filter network; to the intermediate-amplifier grid.

The note begins fading immediately, giving the characteristic percussion effect. This is accomplished in the following manner: when the percussion switch is in the On position, the 6C4 grid (normally held at +25 volts through antispark resistor R53) is connected to the solo manual sixth-harmonic busbar. Depressing a key grounds this 4700-ohm resistor through the key contact and tone-generator filter. This effectively grounds the 6C4 plate.

The tube then becomes essentially an open circuit (being reverse biased at that instant) and isolates the control-tube grid circuit. The grids drift from their normal operating potential, approximately +25 volts, to a cutoff potential of about +15 volts. (NOTE: At that time, the control tubes have –22 volts bias applied to their grid circuits. They reach their cutoff potential when C31 has discharged through R59 and R60.)

The percussion signal is now blocked. No percussion notes can sound until all solo manual keys are released and the control tubes return to their operating point (+25 volts grid potential); this is determined by the time required to charge C31 through R57 and R58.

When either the second- or third-harmonic tab is depressed, the corresponding upper manual harmonic drawbars are disconnected from their lead wires, which become connected to the percussion matching transformer. The sixth harmonic drawbar is also disconnected from its lead wire (grounded through the generator magnets when a key is depressed) which turns off the push-pull control Tube. Because of this the sixth harmonic is not available on the upper manual when percussion is in use.

Precussion decay time may be changed by depressing the Fast Decay tab. When this tab is in the Off position, the only discharge path for C31 is through R60, and the control-tube grids need two and one-half seconds to reach their cutoff potential; when depressed, an additional 1.5 megohms of resistance is shunted across R60, and cutoff potential time is reduced to about half a second.

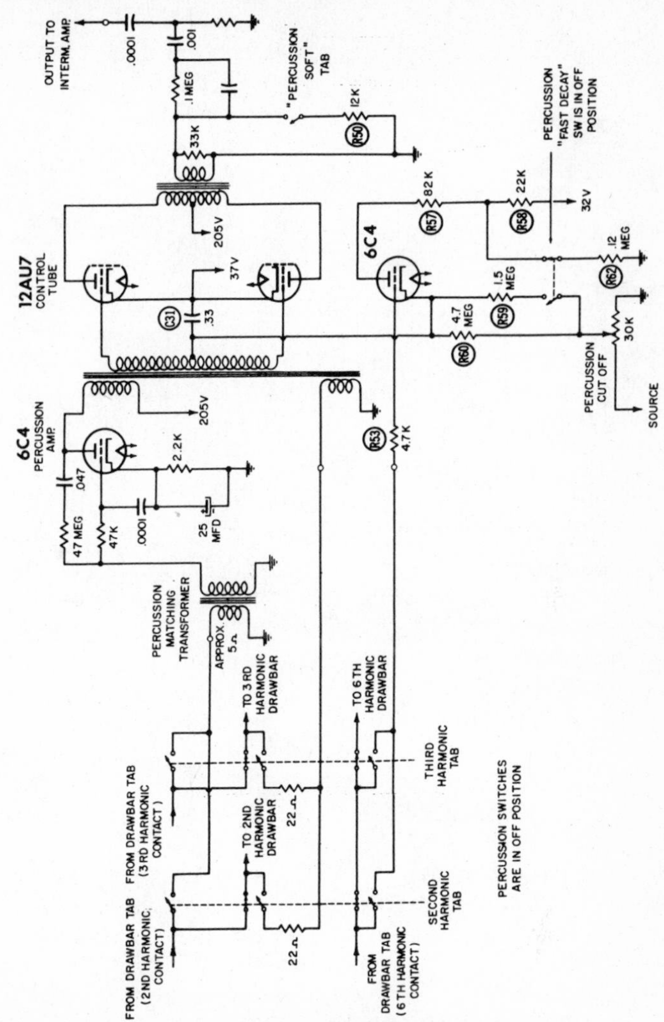

Fig. 6-2. Hammond M-100 percussion system.

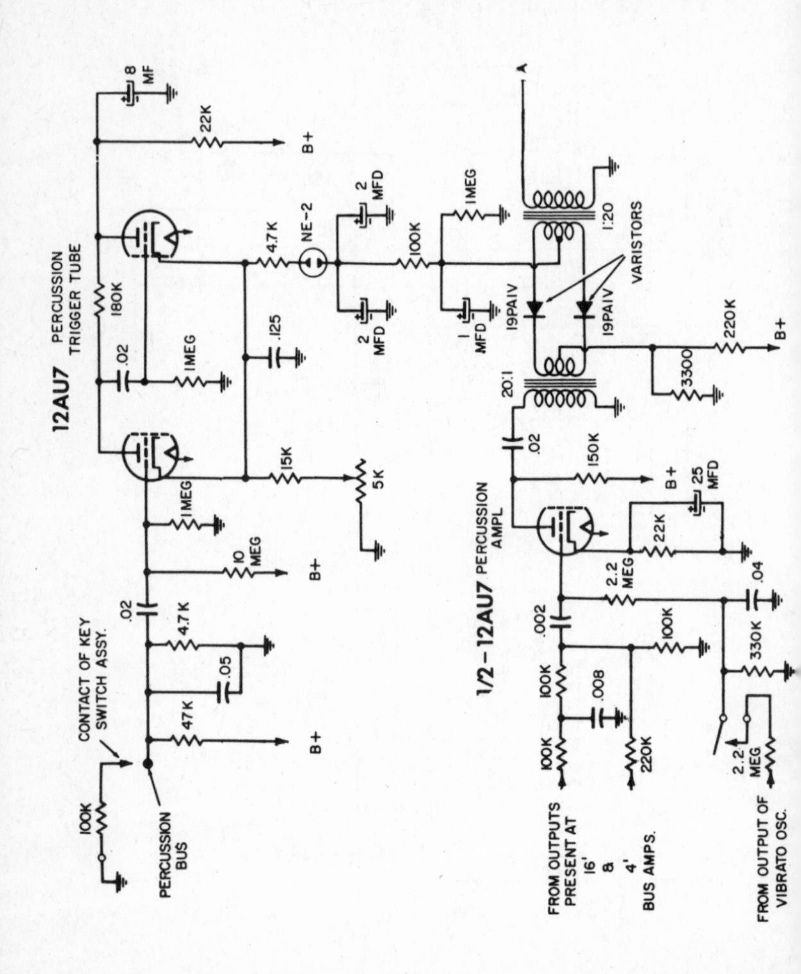

Fig. 6-3. Kinsman Model

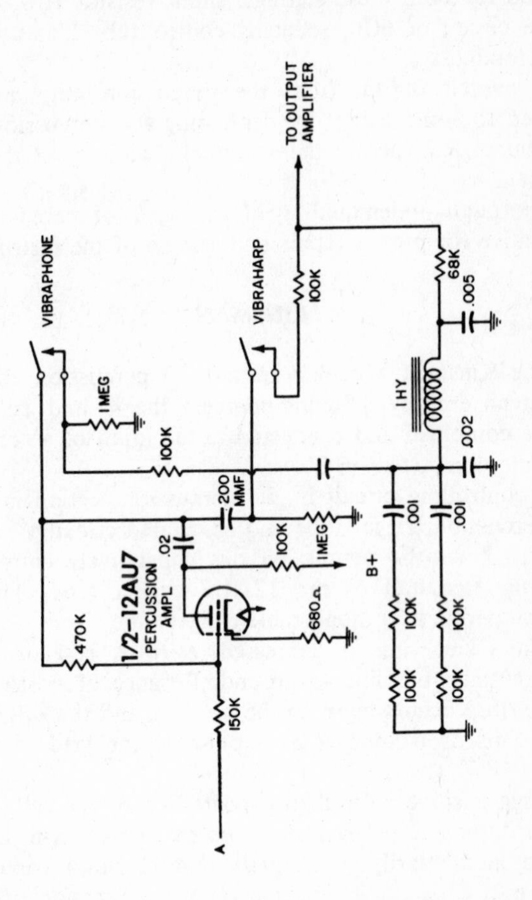

B percussion system.

To maintain the amplitude so that the same amount of output is realized for both these settings, shunt resistor R62 is removed from the circuit of 6C4, reducing control-tube bias and thus increasing loudness.

The overall output from the percussion amplifier may be attenuated to some extent by depressing the Percussion Soft tab, which shunts R50 across the secondary winding of the coupling transformer.

A thorough understanding of this type of percussion circuit is imperative for proper repair and service of the instrument.

KINSMAN

In the Kinsman Model B organ, the percussion effect is obtained in an entirely different manner: the 4′ and 16′ collecting buses are combined and connected to the input of a common percussion amplifier (Fig. 6-3).

The controlling circuit in the percussion section is composed of the percussion trigger tube and associated circuitry. The partial schematic shows the percussion bus capacitively coupled to the grid to the first half of the 12AU7 trigger tube. This tube is biased to operate as a monostable trigger tube.

When a keyswitch is depressed, a 100K resistor is inserted from percussion bus line to ground. Because of positive voltage, a voltage drop occurs between the bus line and the original source voltage. This drop appears as a pulse at the grid of the trigger tube.

A large positive pulse then appears in the tube cathode circuit. Potential difference developed across the NE-2 neon lamp causes it to fire momentarily, leaving the two 2.0-mfd capacitors and single 1-mfd capacitor connected on the other side of the 100K resistor, from there they discharge through the 100K and 1-megohm resistors.

At the same time, whatever signal is present at the 16′ and 4′ bus amplifier outputs is applied to the percussion amplifier and passes through the keying circuit which comprises the two transformers connected back-to-back with the two varistors.

When no charge is available from the neon-lamp capacitors, the varistors are reverse biased so that essentially no signal is allowed to pass. The reverse biasing is maintained with a small positive voltage from the B+ supply.

When the trigger tube fires the neon lamp, the capacitors are quickly charged and the varistors are forward biased, thus allowing the signal to pass. As the capacitors discharge, the signal dies away gradually, leaving no voltage for the plate side of the varistors. The output from this circuit is further amplified in the second half of the percussion amplifier tube; it then passes to two special tone-color circuits on the voicing panel.

Tremolo may be applied simultaneously with the percussion signals by rotating the vibrato control on the voicing panel fully counterclockwise, until a click is heard. A switch is then actuated which turns on a low frequency voltage from the vibrato oscillator. This voltage is superimposed on the percussion-amplifier grid-circuit signals from the 16′ and 4′ bus amplifiers. This action produces an amplitude-modulated tremolo effect on the percussion voices only (similar to that found in the vibraphone or vibraharp).

In this type percussion, any key will trigger a circuit which keys all notes held at the moment. The notes decay if held (similar to a piano); they stop abruptly if the keys are released.

THOMAS

In the Thomas Model V-1 percussion circuit (Fig. 6-4), transistors are utilized throughout, and a one-shot multivibrator controls the gain of a push-pull percussion modulator.

Fig. 6-5 shows the relationship between the percussion circuitry and the associated switching action. This block diagram

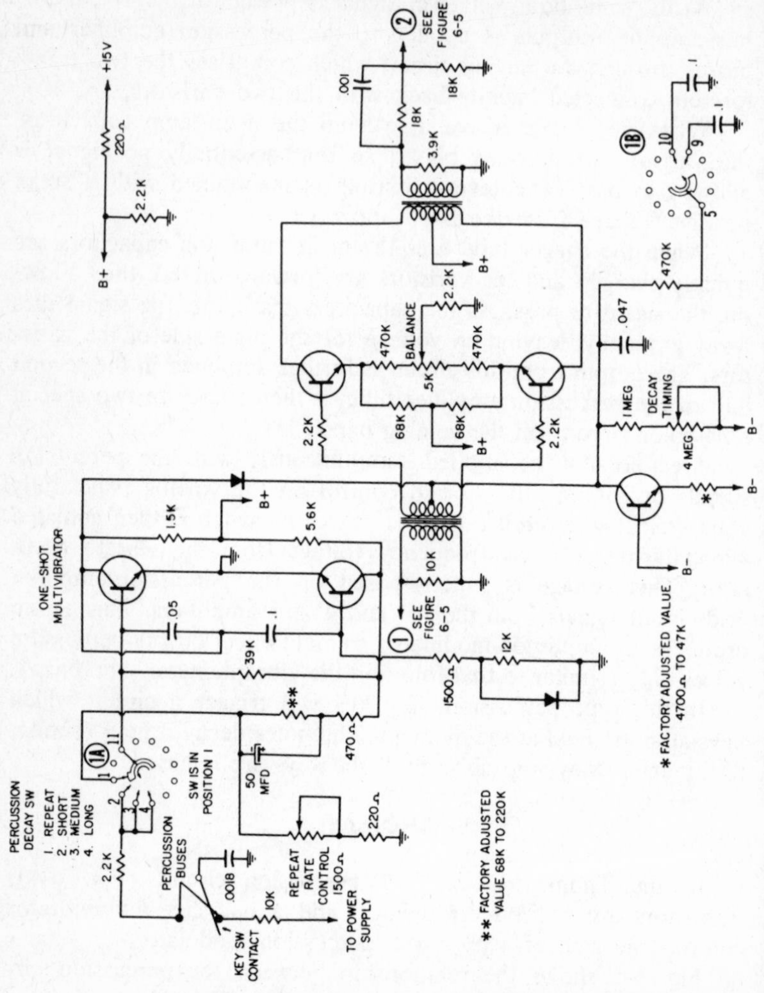

Fig. 6-4. Thomas Model V-1 percussion system.

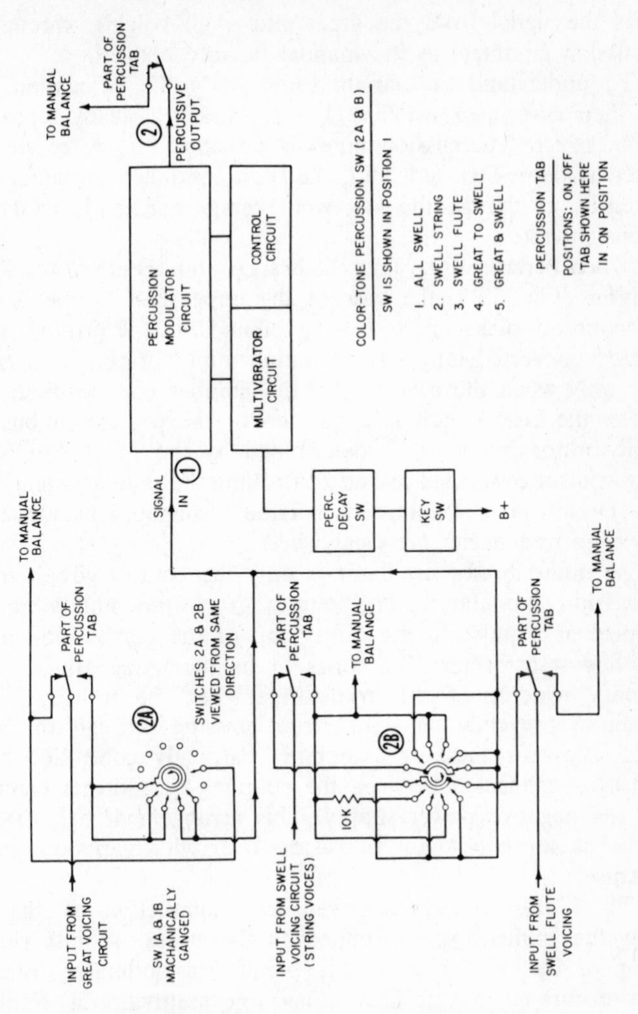

Fig. 6-5. Thomas percussion switching action.

traces the signal from the great and swell voicing, through the percussion circuitry, to the manual balance control.

To understand this circuit fully, study the percussion buses and their associated switches. In this model, a steady repeat rate of the selected percussion notes is possible; i.e., when the key-switch is depressed and held, the tone continues to sound intermittently, as though the key were being repeatedly actuated at a constant rate.

When Percussion Decay switches 1A and 1B are in the Repeat position (Fig. 6-4), the base of the upper half of the one-shot multivibrator picks up its biasing point from the ground, and is thereby converted into a free-running multivibrator. This is possible only when the switch is in the number one position; in all others, the base circuit is connected to the percussion bus. The multivibrator frequency is determined by the 1500-ohm Repeat Rate control connected in and controlling the time constant of the base circuit. As the control is rotated throughout its range, new operating frequencies are established.

The multivibrator oscillator is only the control circuit for the percussion modulator. The output from the multivibrator is coupled as a pulse to the center tap of the percussion-amplifier coupling transformer. The tones to be percussed appear at the primary winding of this transformer, but the transistor cutoff condition prevents the signal from passing through the modulator. Bias for these transistors is partically controlled by the transistor connected between the coupling-transformer center tap and the negative power supply. This arrangement helps stabilize the percussion-modulator transistors over wide variations in temperature.

These transistors are driven into conduction by the pulse from the multivibrators applied to the bases. A fast rise and decay of the base bias on the percussion-modulator transistors then occurs at a rate determined by multivibrator frequency. The tones applied to the primary winding of the coupling transformer then pass through the percussion modulator in "spurts," creating the percussion effect in the output. The collectors of the percussion-modulator transistors are transformer-coupled to the percussion voicing circuits and on to the main amplifier.

We have thus far been concerned with the operation of the percussion circuit when the percussion decay switch is in the Repeat position. Let us now rotate this switch to the Short Decay position. The base circuit of one multivibrator transistor becomes connected to the percussion upper busline through a 2200-ohm resistor. The multivibrator ceases to operate in its free-running state. (The base of the transistor is reverse biased near saturation.) The percussion buses are now the controlling factor in the multivibrator operation.

Notice the keyswitch which connects between the two percussion bus lines. This portion of the circuit is representative of all percussed notes in the instrument. The arm or center contact is operated by depressing a key on the manual. When the key is in the Off position, the .0018-mfd capacitor connected to the center contact charges to a positive potential through the 10K resistor going to the B– supply. When the key is depressed, the switch arm contacts the upper bus and the .0018-mfd capacitor is applied to the base of the one-shot multivibrator. Conduction then stops and a pulse appears at the bases of the percussion modulator.

Tone decay is rapid in this switch position since the only component to hold voltage on the modulator transistor bases is the .047-mfd capacitor connected from the center tap of the coupling transformer to the ground.

To extend decay time, increase the capacity by moving the Percussion Decay switch (section 1B) into position three or four, thereby adding the .1-mfd capacitors to the base circuits of the percussion-modulator transistors, and sustaining the keying voltage to the bases for a longer time.

BALDWIN

Models 46C and 46H

In Baldwin Models 46C and 46H organs, (Fig. 6-6), the percussion assembly is an accessory and, rather than being standard equipment incorporated into the instrument, is purchased separately. The Baldwin provides for simulation of a number of instruments not found on most electronic organs: the harpsichord,

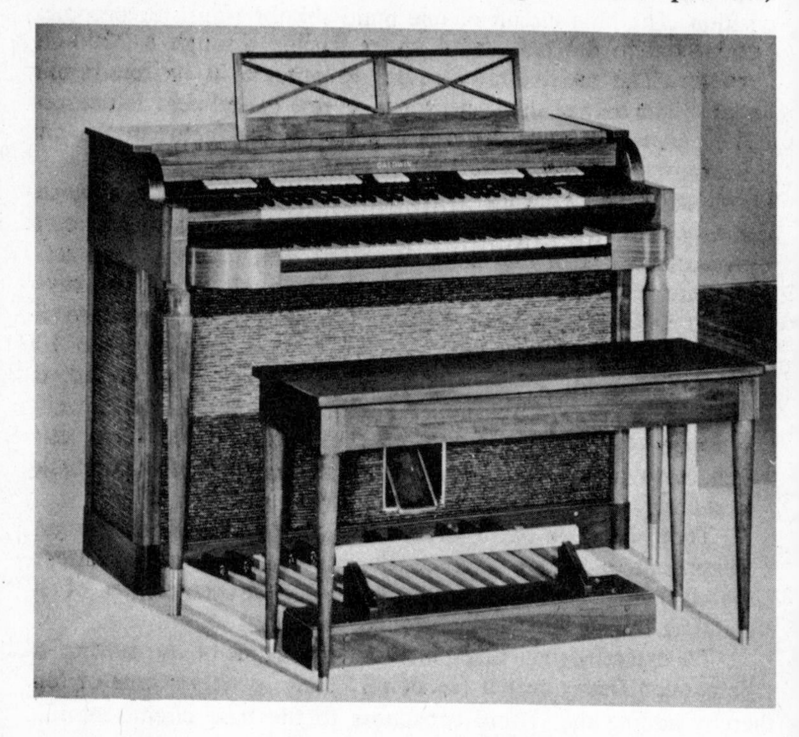

Courtesy Baldwin Organ Company.

Fig. 6-6. Baldwin Model 46.

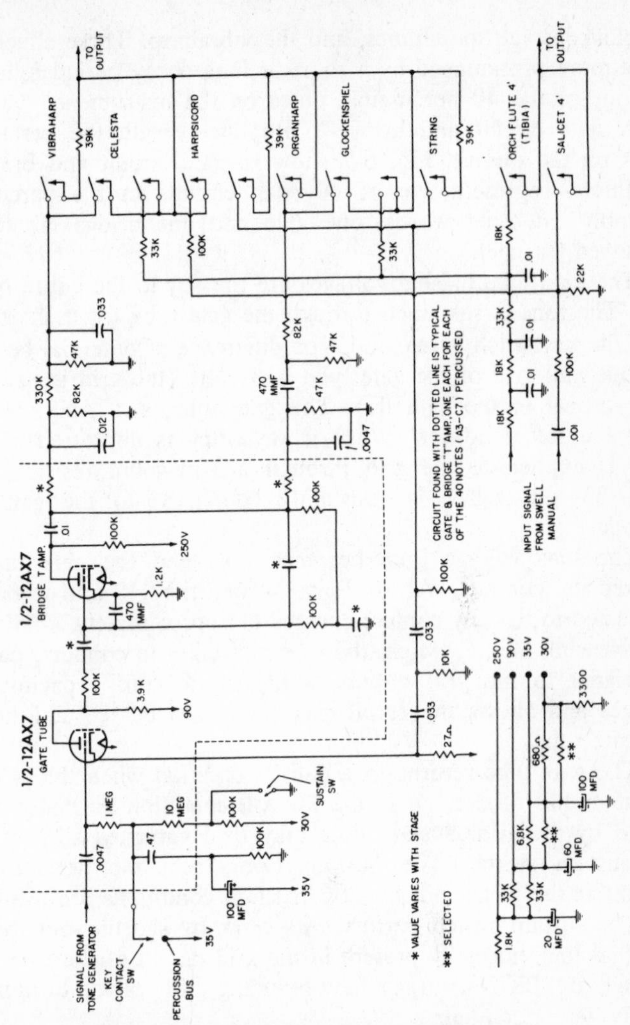

Fig. 6-7. Baldwin 46C and 46H percussion system.

the glockenspiel, the chimes, and the vibraharp. These effects are made more pronounced by a short or long decay period following any one of the 40 percussible notes on the instrument.

A gate circuit and bridge-T amplifier create the percussion effect on the output. Fig. 6-7 shows a gate circuit and bridge-T amplifiers, representative of 40 such circuits in the percussion assembly. In other words, one gate and one bridge circuit are employed for each.

The gate-tube biasing voltages are the key to the entire operation. The tone is sustained through the gate tube for a short time after the keyswitch is released. The difference of potential between cathode and grid of the gate tube is 5 volts (the grid is negative with respect to the cathode). The gate tube, a 12AX7, is in a normal cutoff condition. When a keyswitch is depressed a +35 volts is applied to the grid through a 1-megohm resistor. This same 35-volt source is constantly connected to the gate-tube cathode.

The bias voltage then becomes zero and the gate tube is allowed to conduct. At the same time, the .47-mfd capacitor connected to the key contact charges to approximately +35 volts. On releasing the keyswitch, the tube continues to conduct, passing the signal to the grid circuit, until the .47-mfd capacitor discharges and allows the cutoff-bias voltage to be reestablished in the gate tube.

The gate tube returns to a cutoff condition when the .47-mfd capacitor has discharged to the 30 volt condition normally maintained by the grid. Sustain time may be lengthened slightly with the sustain switch. The Sustain Long-Short tab actuates this switch; as the name indicates two sustain conditions are available.

The sustain switch performs its work by shorting-out the 30-volt bias line, normally present in the grid circuit of the gate tube, through a 100K resistor, thereby reducing grid voltage to approximately zero potential.

The gate-tube cathode continues to be maintained at a positive 35 volt potential, with the grid biased at –35 volts. When a keyswitch is depressed, the 35 volt potential is applied to the gate-tube grid and the tube again becomes zero biased, allowing the selected tone to pass.

When the keyswitch is released, the .47-mfd sustain capactior discharges through the 10-megohm resistor to ground. Discharge is completed much more quickly than in the previous setting because voltage is practically nonexistent in the grid circuit. Thus decay time is noticeably shortened.

In order to maintain a high grid impedance the gate-tube output is connected to a bridge-T amplifier and a portion of the plate and cathode signal is fed back into the grid circuit.

The amplifier output is connected to the various switches, each of which may be actuated by its tab to select the voice or instrument desired. Fig. 6-8 shows the rear view of the percussion assembly in a Baldwin organ.

Model 71-P

The Baldwin Model 71-P organ offers special percussion effects from 36 of its keys, ranging in frequency from *A* at 220 cps to *G#* at 1661.2 cps on the solo manual only. The percussion effects in this model are similar to others in that special instruments may be simulated by the percussion circuits. Such instruments as the vibraharp and organ-harp are readily duplicated by this unit.

To achieve these effects, the signal is controlled, to some extent, through filter networks with a diode gate circuit, so that the duration of sound after release of the keyswitch may be altered. This closely resembles sustain operation; however, the sustain effect, used in conjunction with the filter networks, produces more accurate simulation of these percussion instruments.

Fig. 6-9 shows a diode gate circuit with associated circuitry, representative of 36 such circuits employed in Model 71-P. Normally the diode (D1) is reverse biased, causing it to appear as a

Courtesy Baldwin Organ Company.

Fig. 6-8. Rear view of Baldwin organ.

high resistance to the incoming signal from the generator. Depressing one of the 36 percussible keys will apply a –100 volts to the cathode of diode D1, causing forward biasing of both diodes, and allowing them to conduct and thereby pass the applied signal.

At the same time the .47-mfd capacitor (C1) charges to a –100 volts. When the keyswitch is released and the –100 volts removed, C1 holds the bias voltage on the diode gate circuit until it discharges through the 1-megohm resistor and D1 to ground.

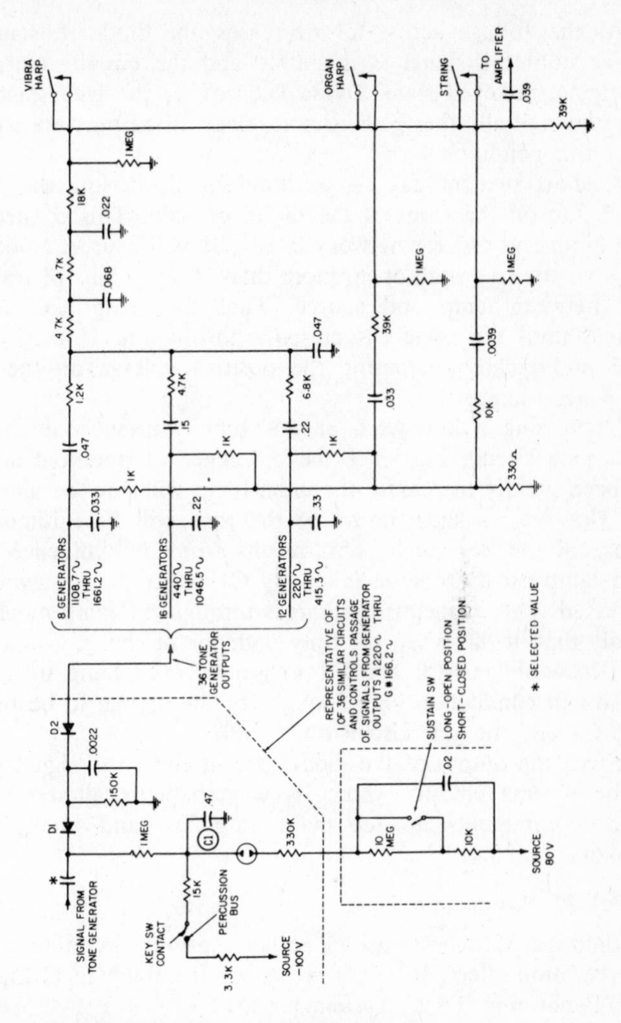

Fig. 6-9. Baldwin Model 71-P percussion system.

As the voltage across C1 decreases, the diode resistance increases until the signal is inaudible and the circuit returned to its original unkeyed state. Diode D2 isolates the gate stage from the outputs of all other gate circuits, since all outputs are common under this condition.

A short sustain may be achieved by depressing the Sustain Switch tab on the front of the organ console. This connects the neon lamp and resistor network to a +80-volt source. Notice that with the sustain switch open, more than 10 megohms of resistance exist between lamp and source. Thus the lamp essentially is isolated until the switch is closed, shorting the 10-megohm resistor and greatly increasing the positive voltage on the anode of the neon lamp.

Depressing a keyswitch at this time will not only bias the diode gate circuit, but since the difference of potential across it has been greatly increased, the neon lamp will now be allowed to fire. However, a short decay of the tone will be initiated after release of the keyswitch. This results from the influence of the neon lamp on the charge taken by C1 when the keyswitch was depressed. This capacitor discharges through the lamp much more rapidly than it did when the only path for discharge was through the 1-megohm resistor and D1 to ground. The lamp in this case remains in conduction long enough for the charge to be removed from C1 and the gate circuit turned off.

From the output of the diode gate circuits, the signal passes: to the voicing circuits where its waveshape is altered to meet voice requirements; to the main amplifier; and finally to the speakers.

Model 71 Panoramic Tone

Baldwin Model 71, uses a rather unusual circuit to obtain a reverberation effect. It is referred to by the Baldwin Company as the "Panoramic Tone" system.

In this system, the organ tones modulate an ultrasonic signal

(20 kc) produced by a triode oscillator. The resultant signals are then used to excite one end of a reflective delay line. Reflected output signal is then removed from the opposite end of the delay line for demodulation and amplification. This is briefly the operation of the unit. Now refer to Fig. 6-10, a schematic diagram, for observation of this circuit in greater detail, and the operation will be discussed more fully.

The organ output tones appear at the grid of the driver amplifier, V1A, and are mixed with the ultrasonic signal from the triode oscillator, V1B. This stage is a conventional triode oscillator whose operating frequency is approximately 20 kc for this application. Notice that the organ signals also appear at the output of a conventional audio amplifier, V2A, just preceding the power amplifier. The organ signals modulate the oscillator output and impress it into the driver-amplifier grid circuit. The result is an unconventionally modulated signal. Since the carrier of the oscillator is suppressed by diodes D1 and D2, only the sidebands appear at the grid circuit.

Thus the signals appearing at the plate of the driver amplifier will contain the signal from the organ generators and the sidebands from the 20-kc triode oscillator. The plate circuit is tuned by L1 to provide maximum gain to the signals appearing at the grid circuit. The output signal is removed from L1 through a .01-mfd capacitor connected to the high side of the coil. The signal present at the other end of the capacitor is connected to a driver crystal which excites the delay line. A similar pickup crystal is connected to the other end of the delay. These crystals are actually transducers since they convert electrical impulses into mechanical impulses, and vice-versa.

The reverberation effect takes place in the delay line, a large spiral-wound coil which causes signals to appear across it at different time intervals on the end opposite that from which the signal was originally fed.

The signals appearing at the output of the delay line are the

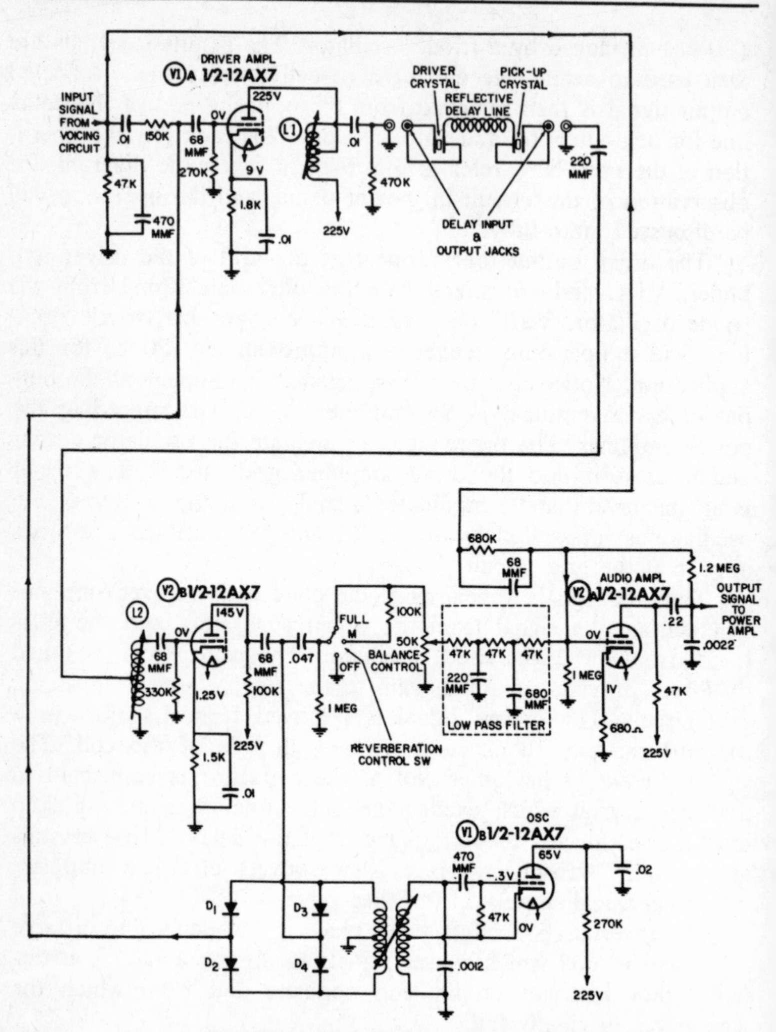

Fig. 6-10. Baldwin Panoramic Tone system.

sidebands which were applied at the grid of the driver amplifier; however, the time delay is considerably greater than if conventional amplification were employed. The reverberated signal appears at the L2 tap in the tuned grid circuit of V2B. The output signal is removed from V2B plate circuit and demodulated by the diode action of D3 and D4.

The demodulated signal is fed through the Reverberation Control switch; to the Reverberation Level control; through a low-pass filter network to remove all 20-kc signal (that might be present at this point from the triode oscillator V1B). The reverberated signal then appears at the grid of V2A and is mixed with the original nonreverberated organ signal. The output from this stage is applied to the power amplifier and, finally, to the speaker system.

ALLEN T-44

The Allen Model T-44 organ percussion assembly like the Baldwin, is an accessory; it does not come as standard equipment with the instrument.

Several percussion instruments are simulated: the banjo, the harpsicord, the vibraharp, and even a celesta effect is available with this organ. Simulation is achieved by a special waveshaping network plus the combination of percussion and sustain effects placed simultaneously on the tone generator output.

The Allen percussion circuit is illustrated in Fig. 6-11. The area within the dotted line is the percussion portion of the circuit where the percussion effect is produced by a continuous breaking of the input voltage of the tone generators. Notice the relay coil (within the dotted area) is activated by the repeat switch, which enables the coil to pick up ground and pull together the relay contacts. The voltage is then removed from the keyswitch so the tone generators have no way to pick up the base bias necessary for operation.

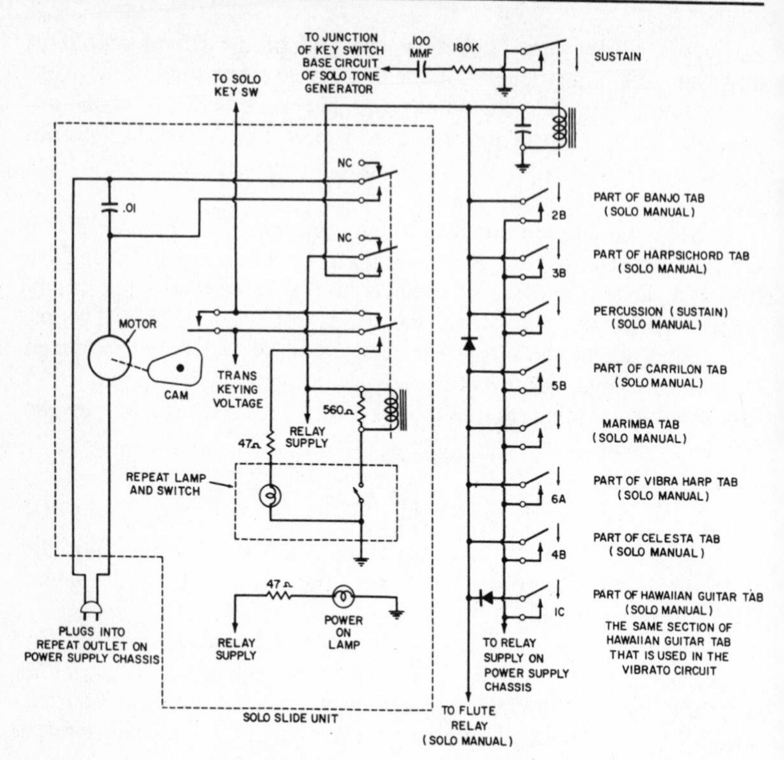

Fig. 6-11. Allen T-44 percussion system.

When the repeat switch is closed, a motor is actuated which drives the cam mechanism at a constant rate, opening and closing the contacts. This in turn opens and closes the bias voltage to the tone generators so they are continually being switched on and off, thus giving the percussion effect to the output. Notice that when a keyswitch is depressed, the base voltage is not fed directly to the tone generators, but rather to the solo keyswitches where it is connected to the bases of the tone generator transistors.

When the percussion keyswitch is selected, the sustain effect is automatically available (through the interconnection of the sustain relay and the percussion relay contacts). When the percussion contacts make, the sustain relay picks up enough voltage to close the sustain contacts. The 180K resistor and 100-mfd capacitor become connected into the base circuit of the tone generator transistors. The percussed tone then emerges with a slight sustain effect added.

The sustain effect is also automatically available to the special percussion voices, shown in Fig. 6-11, by virtue of the special tab-switch hookup. The high side of the sustain relay is connected to the arm of all tab switches from banjo through celesta. To select one of these voices, simply depress the tab and the sustain effect is automatic. Blocking diodes prevent interaction between other associated relay coils.

The tab switches shown here represent only one section of the switch; other sections are encountered in illustrations for the voicing circuit discussion in Chapter 8.

CHAPTER 7

Sustain

On most electronic organs, a note may be held after release of the pedal or manual keyswitch. This feature is called sustain. Some manufacturers associate the term percussion with the sustain condition; this term is not to be confused however, with the use of the term percussion in Chapter 6.

In most models, sustain of one-half to one and one-half seconds is available to the organist. Sustain may be preset by actuating tabs, on the front of the main organ console, mechanically tied to switches that set the condition and length of sustain.

The sustain circuit may vary from one model to the next, but all achieve the same result. Only the sustain time may be different due to variations in circuitry.

Most sustain circuits are composed of a resistance-capacitance network working in conjunction with other components. Some circuits contain a neon lamp, connected as a simple electronic switch, which serves as the signal coupling device.

When the neon lamp is fired, a characteristic low impedance path is developed across it. By controlling the firing point of the lamp, the signal fed to it may be forced to pass when desired. To sustain a note after the key has been released, it is necessary to provide a means of holding the lamp in conduction after release of the keyswitch.

A capacitor is connected to the neon lamp on the side from which voltage is applied to the circuit. When the lamp is energized, the capacitor takes on a charge. After release of the switch, removing the external voltage source, the charge on the capacitor will hold the neon lamp in conduction for a short time. The signal continues passing until the capacitor charge has dropped below the firing point of the lamp.

Another method of obtaining sustain is to feed the tones into a common sustain amplifier, which permits controlling of decay voltage on the plate of a vacuum tube. The sustain-amplifier plate is removed from its voltage source by the keyswitch. When the keyswitch is depressed, however, a capacitor becomes charged and supplies plate voltage to the tube, until finally the charge fades and the tube no longer conducts.

Two methods for sustaining a note or musical tone on the electronic organ have been basically described here. These are by no means the only means to accomplish the sustain effect.

In discussing current organ models it should be emphasized that no one of the circuits involved is necessarily superior to any of the others; each simply offers a method of achieving the same end. Therefore in some cases no reason is given for the use of a particular circuit.

WURLITZER

The Wurlitzer electronic organ offers a typical example of maintaining voltage on a vacuum tube plate after removal of the external voltage source. Signals from the plate continue to pass until the voltage drops to the point where the tube no longer conducts. The sustain effect is then realized, since the signal slowly decays until it is inaudible.

Fig. 7-1 illustrates a tone generator circuit and one of the rotatable rods with which the keyswitch makes contact. This rod extends the length of the keyboard assembly; it is made of *Fiber-*

glas and has a bus bar extending from end to end. When the rod is rotated, this ridge (bus bar) is positioned for making with the key

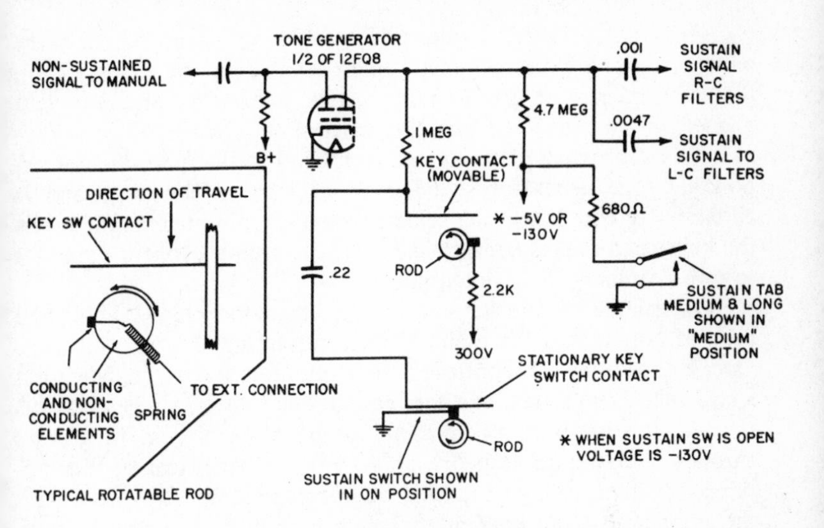

Fig. 7-1. Wurlitzer sustain circuit.

switch contact. External connection to this conductive surface is strengthened for rotation by connecting a spring from the end of the rod to the lead where the external voltage source is applied.

The circuitry in Fig. 7-1 is representative of the 56 circuits in the organ (thus all notes in the instrument can be sustained by the selection of a tab). The sustain tab actuates a switch which connects the .22-mfd sustain capacitor from the key contact to ground. When the rod is rotated into the On position, each of the 56 sustain contacts connects the 12FQ8 tube plate to B-plus through a 1-megohm resistor.

The 12FQ8 is a tone-generator oscillator tube from which two signals are available: the normal, or nonsustained tones, and the sustained tones. (The sustain outputs are also used for intramanually coupling different footage lengths when the sustain switch is in the Off position.)

The sustain switch is also a rotatable rod arranged to make with a stationary key contact. When rotated in the On position, the floating end of all .22-mfd sustain capacitors are grounded and effectivly connected into the active plate circuit. When a keyswitch is depressed, plate voltage is applied to the tube; the corresponding tone generator signal then appears on the plate and is capacitively coupled to the selected wave-shaping networks. When the keyswitch makes contact, the .22-mfd sustain capacitor charges to approximately B+ potential.

On release of the keyswitch, the capacitor charge holds the tube in conduction for a short time, sustaining the selected tone. Decay time may be controlled to some extent by the Medium-Long tab. Depressing this tab actuates a switch which connects the –130 volts, normally present in the plate circuit, to ground through a 680-ohm resistor. This voltage divider causes the applied negative voltage to drop to approximately –5 volts. Thus the applied B+ appears at the plate circuit as a higher voltage, and the tube remains in conduction for a longer period of time.

LOWREY

Lowrey Model LSA (Fig. 7-2) sustain is illustrated in the block diagram, Fig. 7-3, and the partial schematic, Fig. 7-4. The former shows the relationship between the circuits directly affected by the sustain circuitry. Both illustrations should be consulted while tracing the circuit operation.

The first block represents the half of the 6X8 tube which is part of the tone generator assembly. The circuit (Fig. 7-4) represents many similar circuits in the organ. The sustain circuitry output is taken from the 6X8 suppressor grid. The NE-2E is the

Courtesy Lowrey Organ Company.

Fig. 7-2. A Lowrey organ.

neon gate circuit, shown in Fig. 7-3. When a keyswitch is depressed, B+ is applied both to the master-oscillator suppressor grid and the neon lamp. The signal attracted to the suppressor grid is now allowed to pass through the neon gate circuit and on to the formant or voicing network, where it is waveshaped into a specific voice. This action occurs in the nonsustaining condition.

The schematic shows a sustain condition. This model is equipped with a Medium and a Long sustain tab.

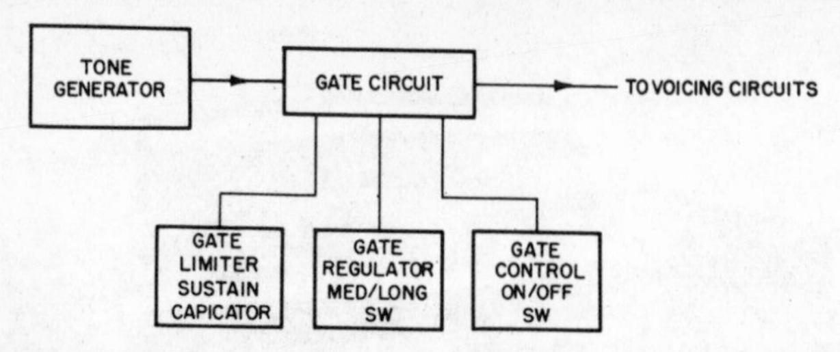

Fig. 7-3. Block diagram of Lowrey sustain circuit.

The On-Off sustain tab when depressed, actuates two separate switches. In the On position, it applies 57 volts to the sustain relay, closes the contacts, and connects the .22-mfd sustain capacitor into the active circuit. Assume that the Long switch is activated. Depress a manual keyswitch and B+ is applied to the generator-

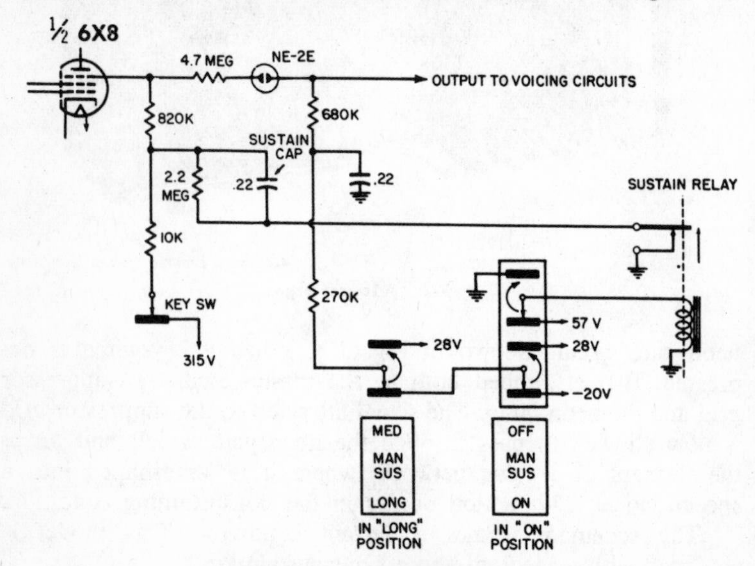

Fig. 7-4. Lowrey sustain circuit.

suppressor grid and the neon gate circuit. At the same time the .22-mfd sustain capacitor charges approximately to source voltage. Notice that on the other side of the neon, a –20 volts is applied to the circuit through the 680K and 270K resistors in series, making the difference of potential developed across the lamp greater than normal. When the keyswitch is released B+ is removed from the suppressor grid and the neon gate circuit. Now the charge remaining on the .22-mfd sustain capacitor is dumped into the circuit, holding the neon lamp in conduction until the voltage across it drops. The voltage decays in an exponential manner and the signal gradually fades away.

The Medium switch initiates the same process. However, a +28 volts, rather than the –20 volts, is applied to one side of the neon lamp. Thus two positive sources are connected to the lamp, reducing the difference of potential developed across the gate circuit. As a result, the voltage across the neon will drop more quickly below the firing point, which means a shorter conduction time and thus a shorter sustain of the tone generator signal.

In some Lowrey models the sustain relay is not included in the circuitry. Instead, the sustain capacitors have their ground connection controlled directly from a tab on the organ console.

KINSMAN

Fig. 7-5 shows a representative sustain circuit for Kinsman Model CP. In this model, only the 8′ tones on the upper manual may be sustained. They are fed through the corresponding bus amplifier or connected individually to sustain keyer circuits, depending on which sustain tab is selected. Thus the upper manual tones may either be sounded normally or sustained for a short time after release of the keyswitch.

Since the sustain feature is all we are interested in at present, let's examine what happens when a sustain condition is brought about.

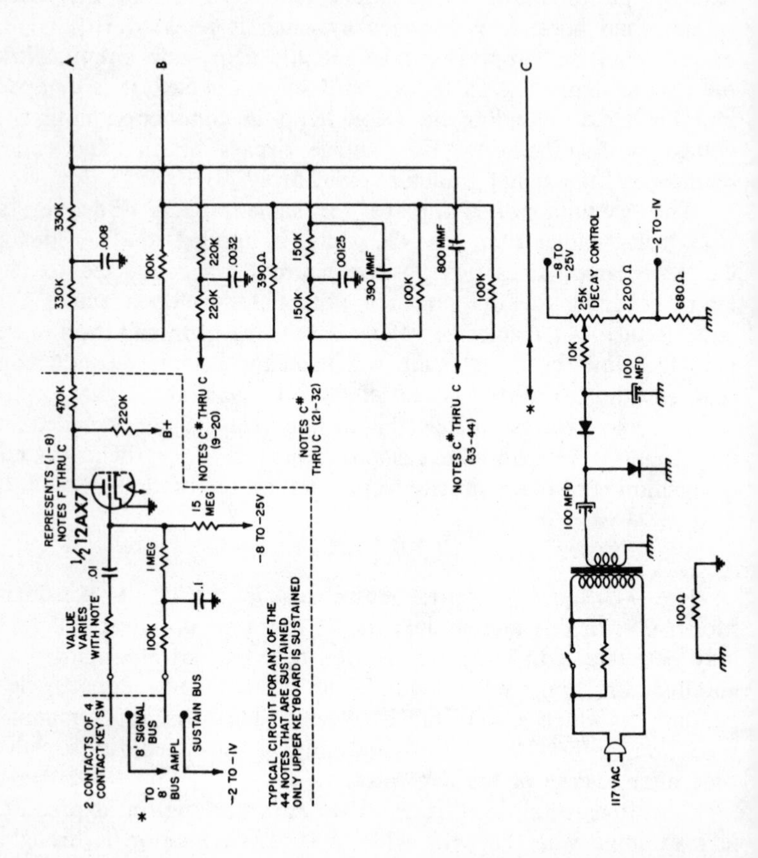

Fig. 7-5. Kinsman sustain

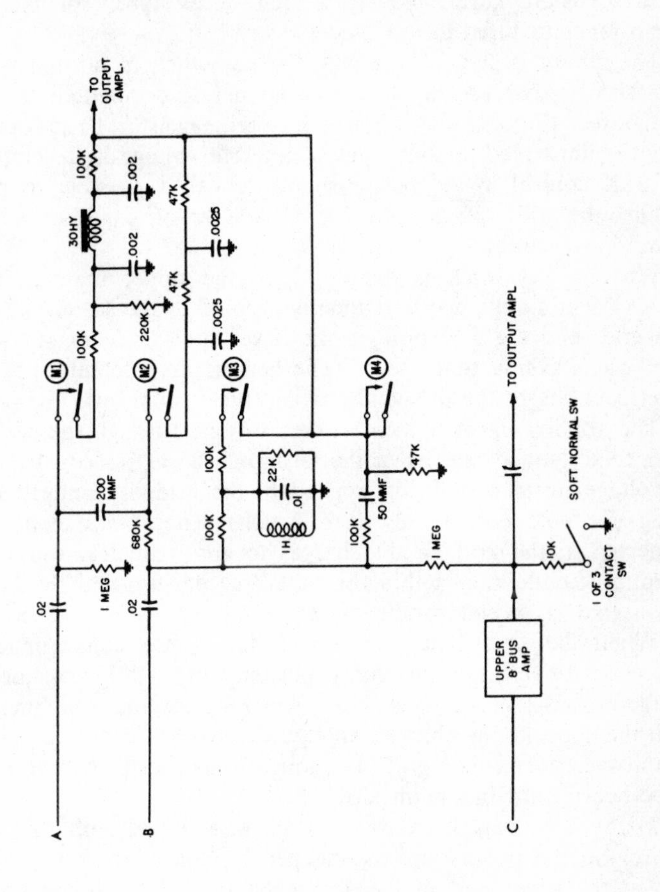
TO OUTPUT AMPL.
100K
.002
30HY
.002
220K
100K
47K
.0025
47K
.0025
M1
M2
M3
M4
200 MMF
680K
1 MEG
.02
.02
A
B
100K
100K
22K
.01
1H
47K
50 MMF
100K
1 MEG
TO OUTPUT AMPL
SOFT NORMAL SW
10K
1 OF 3 CONTACT SW
UPPER 8' BUS AMP
C

circuit.

Half of a 12AX7 (see dotted portion of schematic) is utilized for each sustain keyer, making a total of 22 tubes for the 44 sustain tones featured in this model.

The circuit is shown here with the keyswitch in normal position. The 12AX7 grid is clamped at a negative potential by the voltage fed through the 15-megohm grid resistor. The power supply is illustrated to show how a negative voltage is developed. The 25K control in the power supply makes it possible to pre-establish the grid voltage needed to cause a cut-off condition in the sustain keyer tubes.

When a keyswitch is depressed on the upper manual, two actions occur simultaneously: tone is coupled to the sustain keyer-tube grid; and the grid bias on the keyer tube is decreased to a point where conduction occurs. The actions are accomplished by direct coupling to the 8′ signal bus and the sustain bus.

The applied signal is then allowed to pass through the sustain keyer tube. Notice that when the keyswitch is depressed, the cut-off voltage, instead of being applied to the grid, is connected to a negative potential of only 1 to 2 volts. The .1-mfd capacitor connected in the grid circuit charges to approximately the same potential. Conduction within the tube now occurs, and the keyer tube signal is passed to the output amplifier.

When the keyswitch is released, the .1-mfd capacitor connected at the junction of the 1-megohm and 100K resistors is charged to a –1 or –2 volts. The keyer tube continues to function until the capacitor is charged enough to establish a cut-off condition at the control-tube grid. The tone, decaying slowly, continues to be heard until this point is reached.

Decay time may be varied over a wide range with the 25K control on the percussion voicing panel. This control varies the bias at the lower end of the 15-megohm resistors in the keying units; thereby varying the time required for the grid voltage to reach cutoff after a key is released.

The operating bias on the keying tubes—the bias while a key is depressed—must be kept independent of the decay-control setting. For this reason, the sustain keying bus in the upper keyboard is so connected to the decay control that an increase in the negative voltage at the lower end of the 15-megohm resistors is accompanied by a proportionate, but much smaller, decrease in the negative voltage on the keying bus. While the key is held, the keying-tube grid is connected through a resistor to both these points in such a way that the two effects cancel one another, leaving the grid bias unchanged.

In this particular sustain circuit a slight reverberation effect may be achieved by coupling a small amount of unfiltered signal from the sustain voicing panel to the main voicing panel, through the 8′ Soft-Normal tab switch, and to the input of the 8′ bus amplifier. Thus a portion of the sustain signal is incorporated in all regular 8′ voices on the upper manual, even when no sustain voices are being used. The effect is much like the natural reverberation produced when the Decay control is set for medium or long decay. The effect may be discontinued simply by turning the Decay control to minimum position.

A number of voicing circuits are available to all sustained tones. They are placed into the active circuit by depressing M1, M2, M3, or M4. These circuits are similar to those contained in the main voicing panel.

CONN

To obtain the sustain effect on the output, Conn Models 625 and 540 incorporate a transistor gate circuit working in conjunction with a dual-triode blocking voltage regulator. The only voices sustained in these models are the Flute signals.

Fig. 7-6 shows the sustain-keyer transistor, and the associated blocking voltage regulator which controls its cut-off condition.

The dual triode voltage regulator establishes the base bias

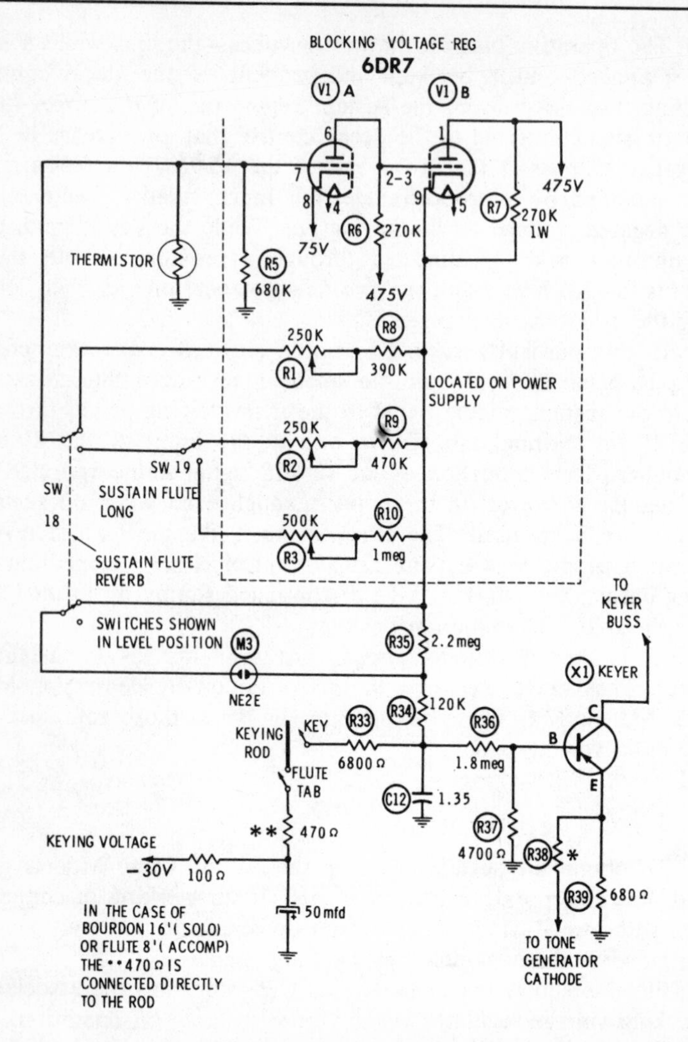

Fig. 7-6. Conn sustain circuit.

for the sustain keyer transistor. Voltage taken from the regulator is self-stabilizing: any voltage error on the cathode circuit is applied to the grid of the first half, and a correcting voltage is applied to the grid of the second half. In this way positive cut-off voltage to the keyer transistor base is controlled to maintain the close tolerance necessary for proper gating of the transistor.

Three positive potentials are available to the keyer-transistor base, one of which is always applied to the transistor when power is applied to the organ. The amount of positive voltage at the base is determined by the setting of the Sustain Flute Long and Sustain Flute Reverb tab switches.

When a sustain condition is desired, the corresponding tab is depressed, rotating a keying rod in the key bus-assembly unit. The rod is then connected to a –30 volt source. A keyswitch is depressed biasing the transistor into conduction, and the flute signal is allowed to pass to the collecting bus. At the same time sustain capacitor C12 charges toward the –30 volts being applied to force the keyer transistor into conduction. On release of the keyswitch the tone continues to sound until C12 discharges through R36 and R37. The time required to charge and discharge C12 depends on the amount of positive voltage from the cathode of the triode voltage regulator. This voltage is controlled to some degree by the Sustain Flute Long and Sustain Flute Reverb switches, which, when actuated, establish a new operating point for the regulator tube and hence alter the voltage applied to the transistor base circuit.

Sustain time may be preset by manually setting R1, R2, and R3. This fixes the length of time required for the keyer transistor to return to cut-off bias after release of the keyswitch, thus allowing control of both decay time and flute-tone attack.

The position of the NE-2E neon lamp within the circuit allows the sustain switches to operate independently of one another. In the position shown, the neon lamp is directly shorting across R35, allowing complete control over each individual sustain timing network.

MAGNAVOX

Magnavox Model A-10 sustain is represented in the block diagram, Fig. 7-7, and the partial schematic Fig. 7-8. Model A-10 offers 44 sustain tones, each removed from the tone generator through a diode keyer. Reverse bias is maintained on the keyer at all times by a +20 volts applied to the cathode.

When a solo manual keyswitch is depressed a –29 volts is connected to the cathode through a 1.5-megohm resistor, and at the same time charges the .39-mfd capacitor connected to one side of the keyswitch. The –29 volts overcomes the +20 volts normally present through the 10-megohm resistor, and the diode is forward-biased. The selected tone is now allowed to pass to the sustain follower. This is an impedance-matching amplifier providing a low-impedance output to the base of the 8′-solo sustain amplifier. The selected tone continues to sound until the .39-mfd capacitor has discharged and the diode keyer returned to cut-off condition. In this model, the sustain bus (located in the key-switch assembly) is in the active circuit at all times. Also, the sustain follower and 8′-solo sustain amplifier function at all times, regardless whether a sustain or non-sustain condition is in effect.

Switching of the sustain signals follows the output of the solo sustain amplifier. This arrangement allows for special voicing of the Vibra-Harp and String instruments. Thus, the sustain effect may be applied simultaneously to these voices to give the necessary sounding.

Notice that the sustain selector-switch (activated by a tab on the control panel) selects only the 8′ tone path to the voicing circuits. In the nonsustain position, the solo 8′ tones are taken directly from the 8′ bus amplifiers. Switching to the sustain condition removes the signal from the collector of the 8′-solo sustain

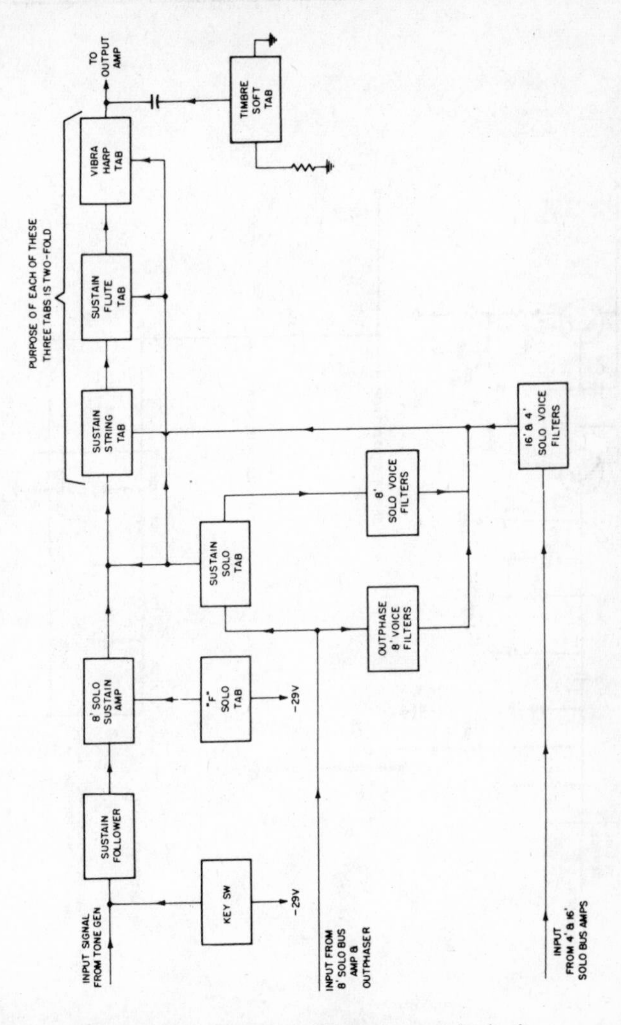

Fig. 7-7. Block diagram of Magnavox sustain circuit.

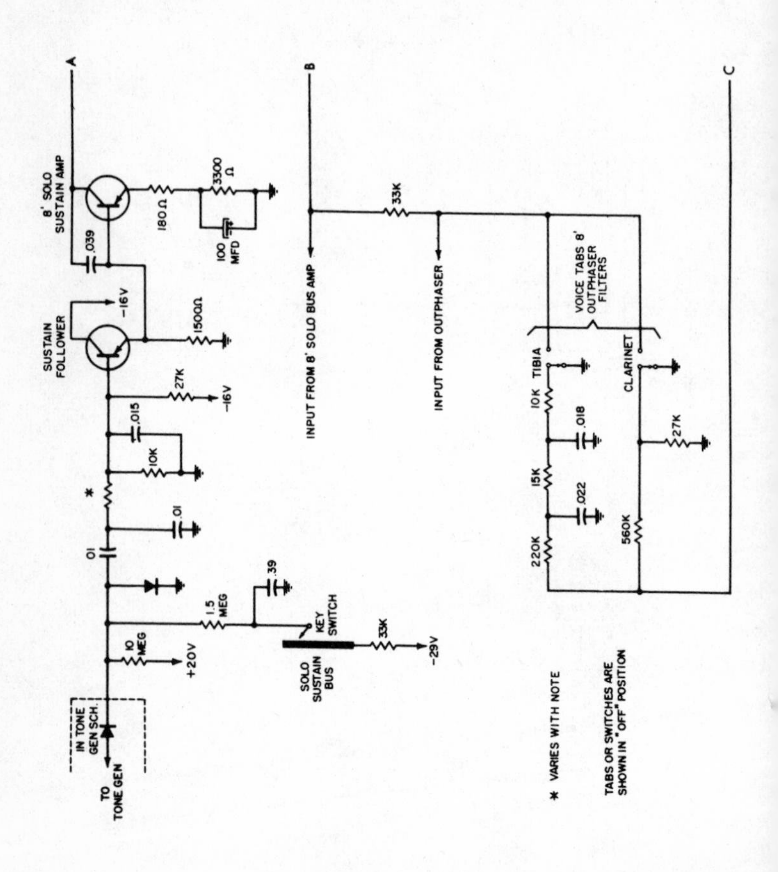

Fig. 7-8. Magnavox sustain

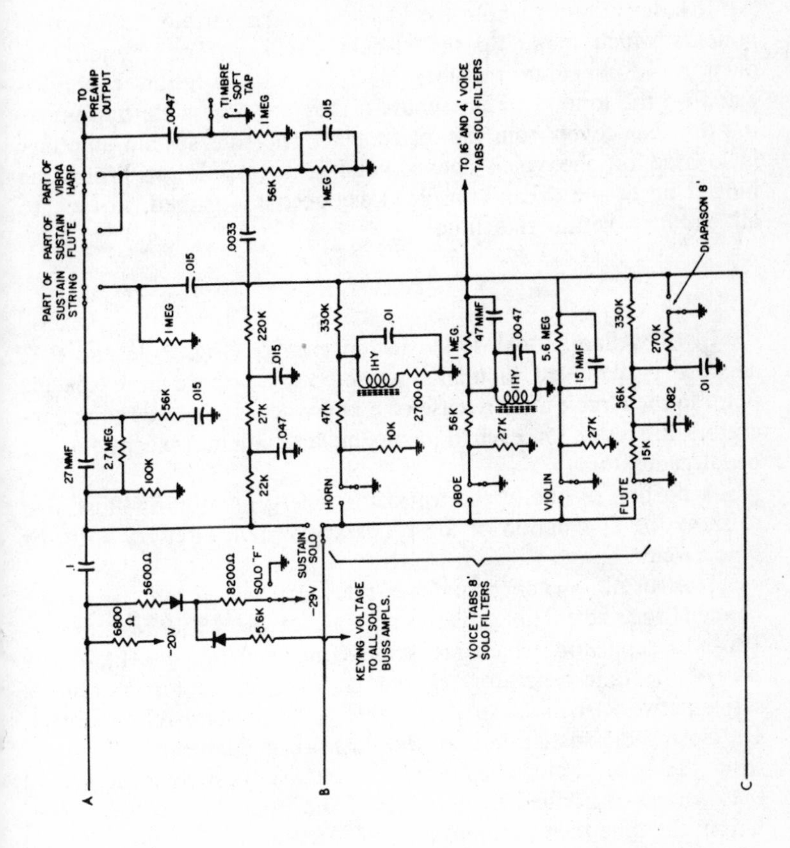

TO PREAMP OUTPUT
PART OF VIBRA HARP
PART OF SUSTAIN FLUTE
PART OF SUSTAIN STRING
TIMBRE SOFT TAP
.0047
1 MEG
.015
56K
1 MEG
.0033
.015
1 MEG
220K
.015
27K
.047
22K
56K
.015
2.7 MEG.
27 MMF
100K
.1
5600Ω
6800 Ω
-20V
8200Ω
SOLO "F"
SUSTAIN SOLO
-29V
5.6K
KEYING VOLTAGE TO ALL SOLO BUSS AMPLS.
HORN
330K
.01
1HY
2700Ω
47K
10K
TO 16' AND 4' VOICE TABS SOLO FILTERS
1 MEG.
47 MMF
.0047
1HY
56K
27K
OBOE
5.6 MEG
15 MMF
27K
VIOLIN
330K
270K
.01
56K
.082
15K
FLUTE
DIAPASON 8'
VOICE TABS 8' SOLO FILTERS
A
B
C

circuit.

amplifier through a .1-mfd capacitor and applies it to the corresponding voicing circuits, as selected.

It is important to note the location of the various major components which make up the sustain circuitry. The .39-mfd capacitor, 1.5-megohm resistors, and the sustain-follower are located on the tone generator chassis; they are accessible by removing the rear cover from the instrument. The solo sustain-amplifier is located on the voice chassis, and is accessible by lifting the hinged lid of the organ console. Easy access is gained, in fact, to all circuitry within this model.

ALLEN

In the Allen Model T-44 sustain circuit, (Fig. 7-9) the R-C network is arranged to maintain temporary voltage at a specific point in the circuit after release of a keyswitch. Individual tone generators are used for each note in the instrument (except for the pedal generators).

A portion of one of the transistor tone generators is illustrated to show the association of the necessary sustain circuitry with the base circuit.

The sustain switch actuates a relay coil which pulls the relay contacts together. This grounds one end of the 180K resistor and 100-mfd capacitor, which are series-connected into the input circuit of the tone-generator transistors. Each generator contains a series network such as this, returning to the sustain relay contact. On closing the sustain switch, the network is connected effectively from the base circuit to ground. When a keyswitch is depressed bias voltage is applied to the base of the transistor, causing oscillation; the tone then becomes audible. Simultaneously, the 100 mfd capacitor charges to approximately the same value as the bias voltage. When the keyswitch is released the tone continues to sound until the 100-mfd capacitor discharges and the transistor no longer has sufficient base bias voltage to maintain oscillation.

Thus, the tone decays slowly until it is inaudible.

The sustain relay may be actuated either by the sustain switch or by any one of a number of other voicing switches. In Chapter

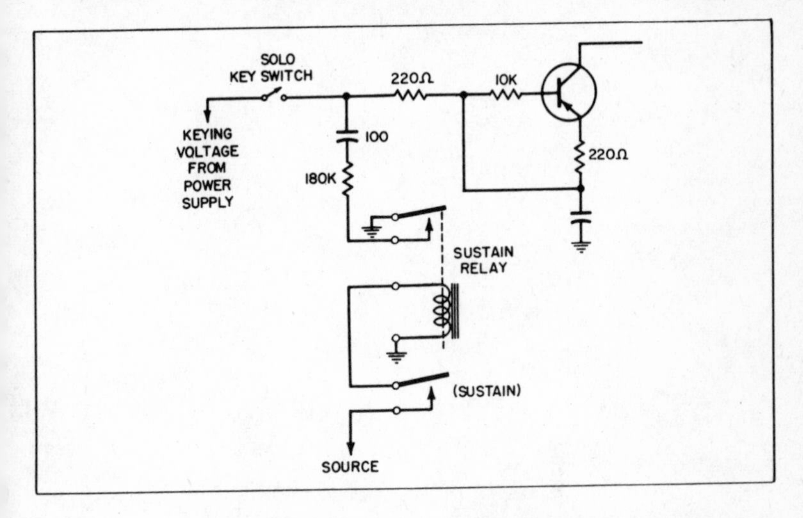

Fig. 7-9. Allen sustain circuit.

6 (Percussion) we learned that several of the percussion voices will actuate the sustain relay when the appropriate tab is selected.

Because of their close relationship, it is impractical to discuss the pedal sustain circuits separately from their associated generators and keyswitches; the subject of pedal sustain is covered, therefore, in Chapter 3; the above analysis was limted strictly to the manual tones.

CHAPTER 8

Voicing

Voicing is the term commonly used to describe simulation—the imitation of various instruments on the electronic organ. Voicing has already been mentioned several times and its importance is quite evident. Without voicing, all organ sounds would be identical.

If the imitation of a trumpet or oboe sound is not exact, when the appropriate tab is switched, remember that the sounds are achieved electronically. Although the illusion may not be that of a musician playing in the same room, the simulation is quite close.

In some organs manufactured today, the voicing circuits comprise a large portion of the circuitry and are apparently complex in their wiring. In spite of this, most of them are easily understood. A simple voicing circuit may consist of only resistance and capacitance; or it may comprise resistance, capacitance, and inductance in varied combinations.

The voices are established by switches that insert different values of resistance and capacitance—or, in some cases, inductance—into the signal path from the tone generator to the power amplifier.

To change voices in the organ, it is only necessary to alter the shape of the waveform from the tone generator. The voicing circuit, in other words, is nothing more than an ordinary waveshaping network.

An electrical waveform is composed of an infinite number of harmonics which determine the final waveshape. To alter the waveform requires filtering out unwanted harmonics or overtones from the original waveform. For this reason many organs derive a sawtooth waveform from their generating system; its rich harmonic content makes possible the easy simulation of a large number of instruments at the output.

The technician should be familiar with the electronic simulation process so he can learn to detect trouble in the voicing circuit as quickly as in any other part of the organ.

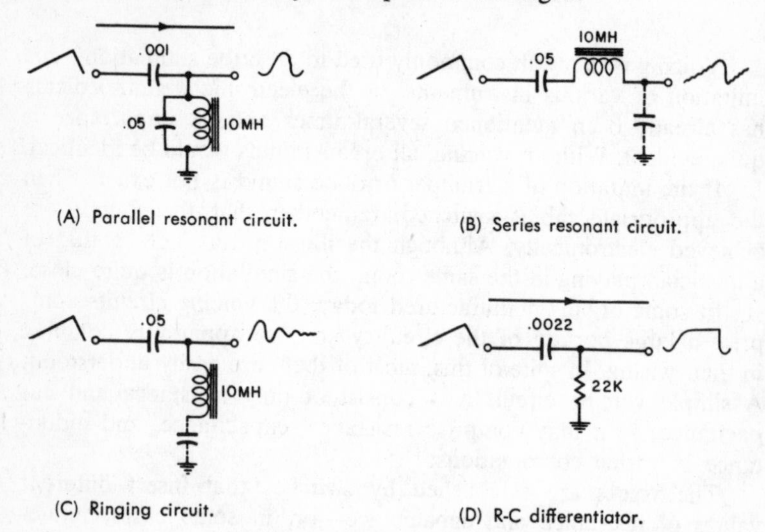

(A) Parallel resonant circuit.

(B) Series resonant circuit.

(C) Ringing circuit.

(D) R-C differentiator.

Fig. 8-1. Waveshaping networks.

Fig. 8-1 shows a number of waveshaping networks, each with a sawtooth voltage waveform being applied to the circuit. Notice the effect on the various components in each case. These circuits are typical tone generating systems widely used to produce a sawtooth waveform from the output.

In Fig. 8-1A, the sawtooth waveform is being applied to a parallel resonant circuit consisting of an iron-core inductance with a capacitor. Notice the output waveform is close to a sine wave. Since this parallel network is a maximum impedance to its resonant frequency and is a low impedance path to ground for all other frequencies, the output waveform will contain just frequencies to which the L-C combination is resonant.

In Fig. 8-1B, the sawtooth waveform is being applied to the same inductance and capacitance connected in a series-resonant circuit whose characteristic impedance is exactly opposite the parallel circuit in Fig. 8-1A. The series-resonant circuit in Fig. 8-1B is at minimum impedance at resonance, while the parallel resonant circuit is at maximum.

The output waveform still looks like the sawtooth, except the top is rounded off slightly, and a ripple is apparent along the sides. The ripple is due to the various sawtooth harmonics within the tuned-circuit resonant frequency. The harmonics are emphasized in the output, because the tuned circuit offers little resistance to frequencies within the resonant range of the series inductance and capacitance.

The network in Fig. 8-1C is connected the same as that in Fig. 8-1B, except the output waveform is taken from the top of the inductance, next to the generator coupling capacitor. Fig. 8-1C is also the same as Fig. 8-1A, except the coil and capacitor are connected in a series-resonant circuit. This gives the effect of ringing in the output waveform, since no termination is available to frequencies within the series-circuit resonant range. Since the circuit is constantly going from minimum to maximum impedance, oscillations are set up with the L-C combination. When oscillation occurs, the major waveform takes on the appearance of a sine wave. By proper filtering, oscillations may be damped almost completely, and the output waveform will be sinusoidal.

Probably the most common method of changing a waveform is with R-C networks. In a waveshaping circuit, the capacitor and resistor are selected so the charge and discharge rate of the capacitor may be controlled. Amplitude and frequency of the applied signal determine the size of the integrator or differentiator circuit.

The typical resistance-capacitance network, shown in Fig. 8-1D, is actually a differentiating circuit: the output waveform is altered from the input sawtooth waveform applied to the circuit. This is accomplished by choosing the resistor and capacitor combination that will maintain a short time constant with respect to the input signal, when the sawtooth voltage waveform is applied. In addition to the change in waveform, a phase lag occurs in the output signal.

WURLITZER

Wurlitzer Models 4100 and 4102 contain excellent examples of both R-C and L-C circuits in the formant or voicing circuits of the organ. A portion of each circuit is shown in Fig. 8-2.

A number of tones, such as orchestra flute 4′ and violin 4′, utilize resistors and capacitors to give the necessary waveshape to the tone generator signal. The signals to the voicing circuits are removed from the percussion bus in the main tone-generator assembly and connected to the R-C and L-C filters simultaneously.

Each voice is selected by depressing its corresponding tab; this actuates a switch which grounds or breaks ground through the filter network.

Tones such as the flute 8′, trumpet 8′, and oboe 8′ are developed through tuned-filter amplifiers, two of which are shown in Fig. 8-2. These amplifiers use inductance in conjunction with capacitors to do the necessary filtering. Tunable chokes provide the inductance to obtain the correct output waveform.

Most voicing circuits consist of networks that shape the waveform from the main generating system. This type of waveshaping is possible, however, only when the output waveform from the

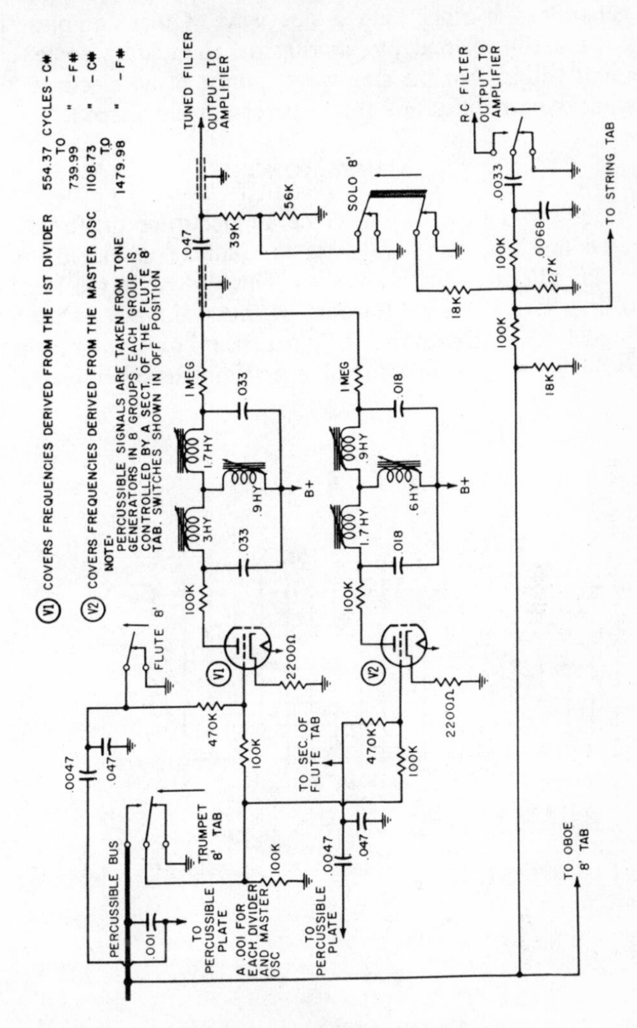

Fig. 8-2. Wurlitzer voicing circuit.

tone generators is other than a sine wave. Other complex waveforms are easily shaped by filtering or attenuating some of the harmonics within; but the sine wave, purest of all electrical waveforms, lacks harmonics and therefore cannot be shaped.

HAMMOND

The only practical way to voice an electronic organ where all generated tones are sine waves is to combine in varied amounts rather than filter out, the harmonics. This is done in the Hammond L-100 and M-100 Series. Because of the sine wave output of the mechanical tone generators, it is necessary to combine the harmonics in varied amounts to voice or simulate other instruments.

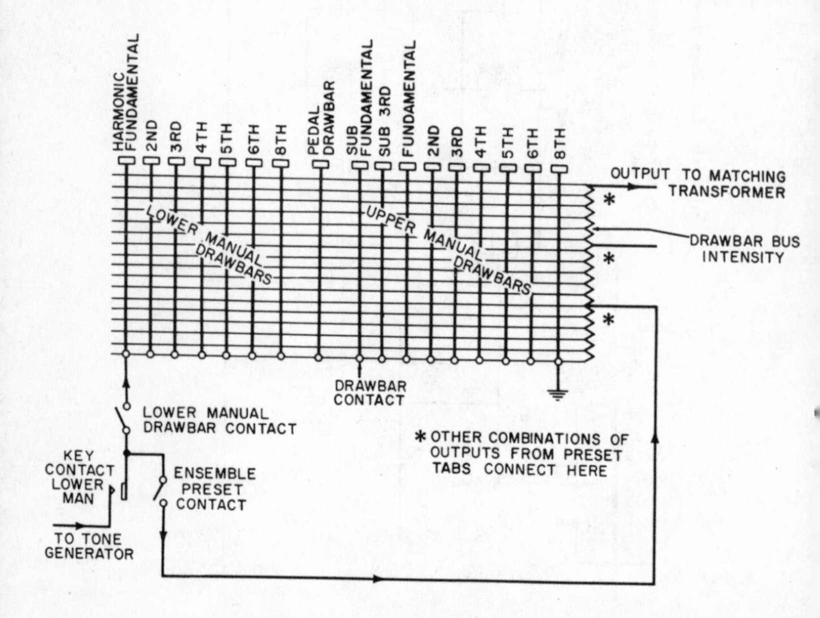

Fig. 8-3. Hammond drawbar switch circuit.

A wide voicing range is available to the organist through the mixing system provided by manipulating the harmonic drawbar tabs (Fig. 8-3) on the front of the organ console. The lower manual has seven drawbars, the upper manual has nine. The drawbar near the center of the schematic combines pedal and manual tones so that the two may be sounded together.

The drawbars are slid in and out to mix the fundamentals and harmonics, or overtones, in the desired proportions. The distance the bar is pulled out determines the strength of the corresponding harmonic. With the drawbar all the way in, the harmonic it represents is absent. Neither manual will sound unless at least one drawbar is pulled partially out. All drawbars make with the ground bus unless they are pulled out far enough to make with one of the seventeen bus bars.

The drawbar contacts are constructed so that as the drawbar is slid out, the contact touches the next busbar before it is removed from the present one. Thus the contact is touching one busbar at all times, affording smooth change in volume. In the same way, the over-riding of the drawbar contacts prevents "dead spots" in the output.

All seventeen busbars extend the length of the drawbar assembly and are connected to the low-impedance primary winding of a matching transformer. Signals from the high-impedance secondary winding are connected to the preamplifier. The matching transformer is located in the preamplifier chassis.

ALLEN

Allen Model T-44 contains almost all types of voicing circuits found in the modern electronic organ; both R-C and L-C types are found in a wide variety of circuitry.

In the Allen organ, the sinusoidal waveform from the tone generators may be forced through the network which alters its shape and thus prepares it to meet the timbre quality of the particular voice.

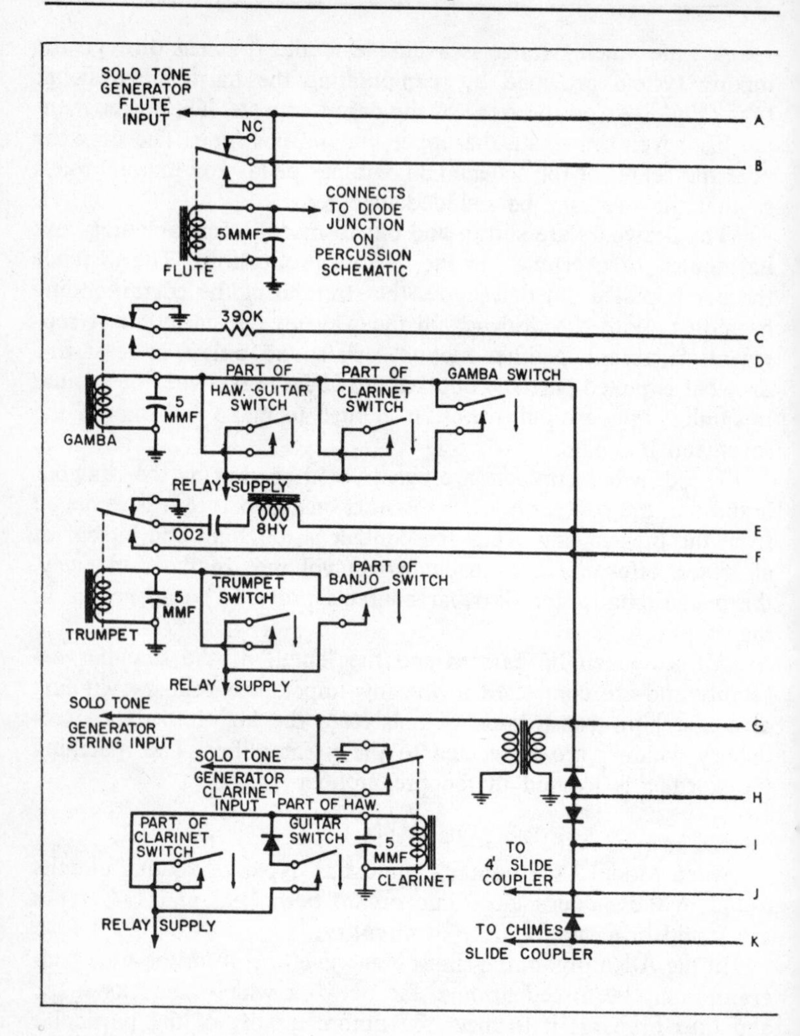
SOLO TONE
GENERATOR
FLUTE
INPUT
NC
A
B
CONNECTS
TO DIODE
JUNCTION
ON
PERCUSSION
SCHEMATIC
5MMF
FLUTE
390K
C
D
PART OF
HAW. GUITAR
SWITCH
PART OF
CLARINET
SWITCH
GAMBA SWITCH
5
MMF
GAMBA
RELAY SUPPLY
.002
8HY
E
F
TRUMPET
SWITCH
PART OF
BANJO SWITCH
5
MMF
TRUMPET
RELAY SUPPLY
SOLO TONE
GENERATOR
STRING INPUT
G
SOLO TONE
GENERATOR
CLARINET
INPUT
PART OF HAW.
GUITAR
SWITCH
PART OF
CLARINET
SWITCH
5
MMF
CLARINET
H
I
TO
4' SLIDE
COUPLER
J
TO CHIMES
SLIDE COUPLER
K
RELAY SUPPLY

Fig. 8-4. Allen

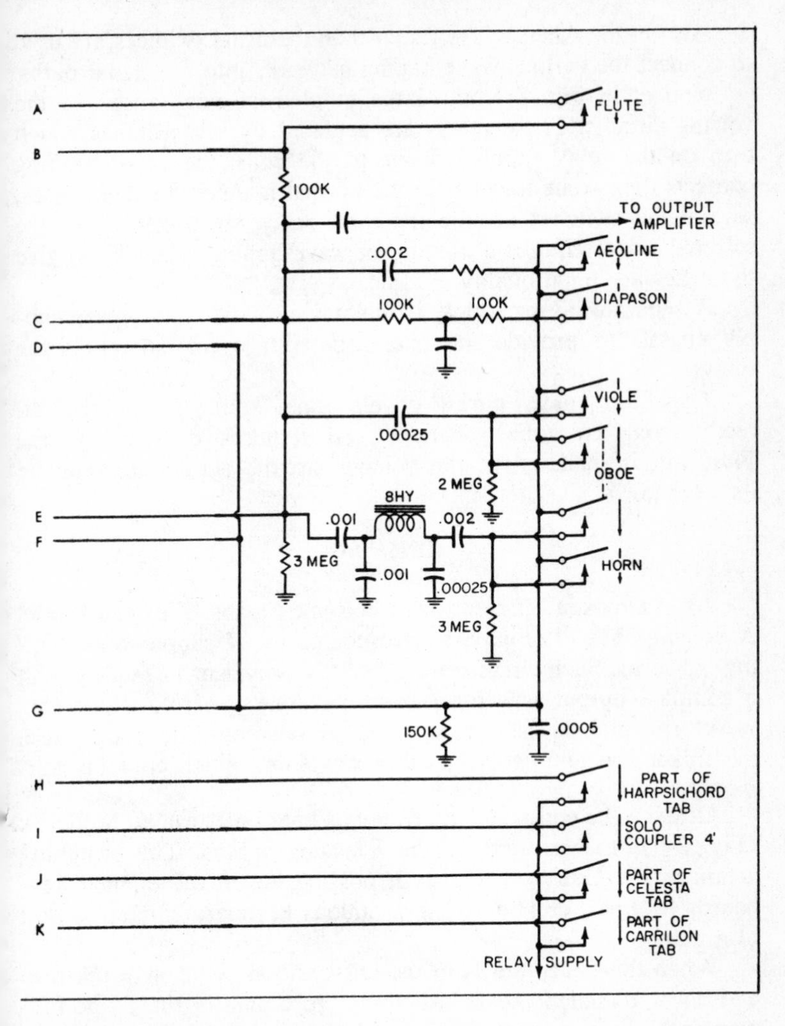

voicing circuit.

Also in the Allen, relays, rather than the usual swithces, are used to connect the various waveshaping networks into the signal paths.

Notice, in Fig. 8-4, the large number of relays used in the voicing circuits. These relays are actuated by tab switches which turn on the relay supply voltage to the coils; the corresponding contacts then come together in the normal manner. In some cases, several tab switches actuate the same relay, since oftentimes the selected voice requires a mixture of waveshaping networks to give the necessary tonal quality.

A separate power supply is maintained within the power supply chassis to provide the necessary voltage for operating the relays.

The flute voice, purest of all organ sounds, is taken directly from the tone generator and requires no voicing; the Flute tab is included in the voicing circuits simply to expedite its selection.

KINSMAN

As in almost all present-day electronic organs, Kinsman Model A voicing circuits (Fig. 8-5) are composed of simple waveshaping networks. Such circuits are especially prevalent in models with a complex output waveform from the tone generator. Complex waveforms include the square wave, the sawtooth, the sharp pulse, the spike, and almost every other waveform which contains harmonics.

Observe the construction of the bus lines on Kinsman Model A (Fig. 8-6), the smallest of the Kinsman organs. The switching action of the Unify tab makes it possible to tie the manual keyboards together, creating one continuous keyboard similar to that of a piano.

When the Unify tab is in the Off position, as shown, the solo and accompaniment keyboard buses are separate; the 8′ accompaniment bus is at rest and the 4′ bus is connected to a load re-

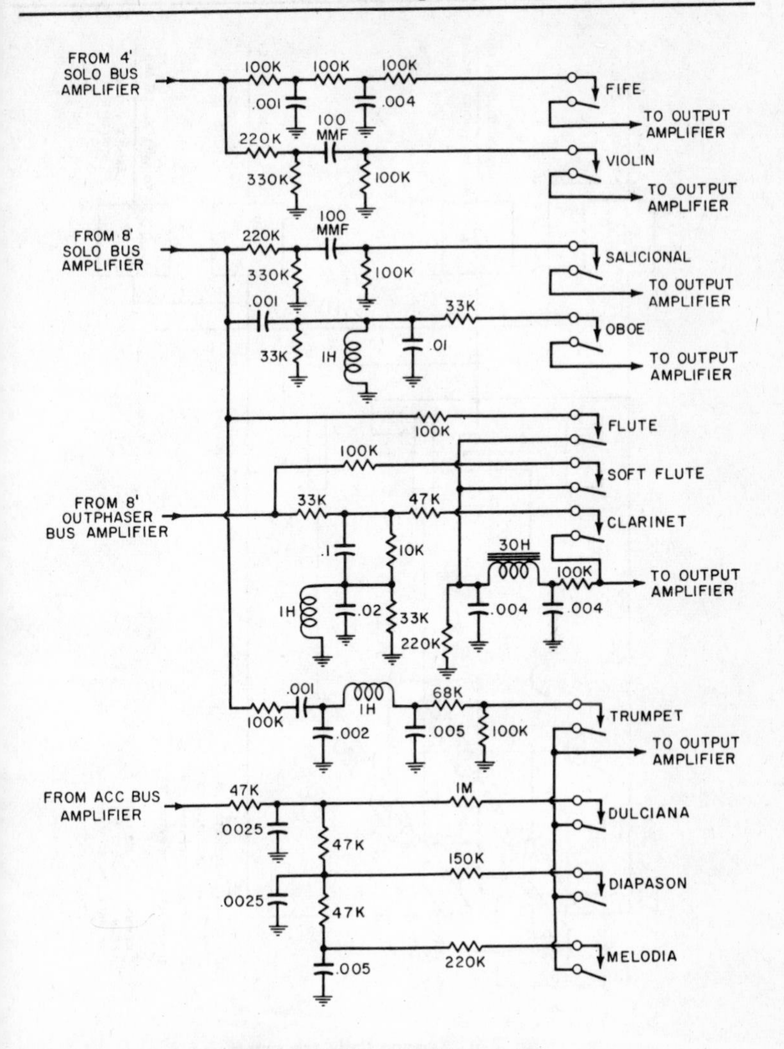

Fig. 8-5. Kinsman voicing circuit.

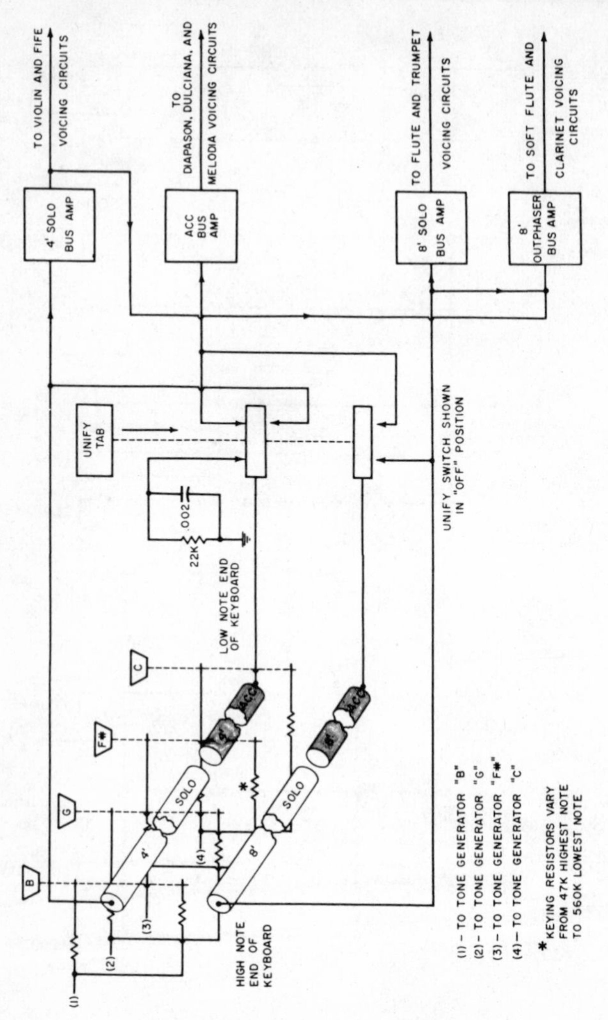

Fig. 8-6. Kinsman Unify tab system.

sistor and to the bus amplifier accompaniment input. Thus, the accompaniment voices sound a 4′ pitch—an octave higher than might be expected from the physical position of the keys. This is equivalent to having an accompaniment keyboard overlapping the lower end of the solo keyboard and sounding an 8′ pitch. In this way the accompaniment voices sound the pitch for a separate keyboard. Six of the solo voices sound an 8′ pitch and two sound a 4′ pitch. These voices sound only when the keys on the solo keyboard are played.

Placing the Unify tab in the On position joins the two 8′ buses and the two 4′ buses creating the one continuous keyboard. At the same time, the input to the accompaniment section of the bus amplifier is shifted from the 4′ accompaniment bus to the 8′ combined bus. Thus, the accompaniment voices are transformed into additional buses for the keyboard. Such an arrangement adds greatly to the flexibility of the instrument.

THOMAS

Fig. 8-7 shows how the flute tones are developed in Thomas Model V-1. Notice the large number of L-C networks utilized to derive the waveform needed to simulate the sound of the flute.

Being almost a pure sine wave, the flute voice is derived from a complex tone by constructing a low pass filter; in this way, the higher harmonic content of the complex waveform is attenuated and only the fundamental frequency allowed to pass through the filter network.

The circuits shown in this illustration shape the flute tone before it is passed to the transistor amplifier which raises the level of the signal. From there the signal goes to the percussion circuit, where it is sounded with the percussion effect.

The similarity between voicing circuits makes for a rather limited discussion. The main thing to remember is the complex waveform derived in the tone generators is the prime factor in determining the type of waveshaping network to be used for simulation.

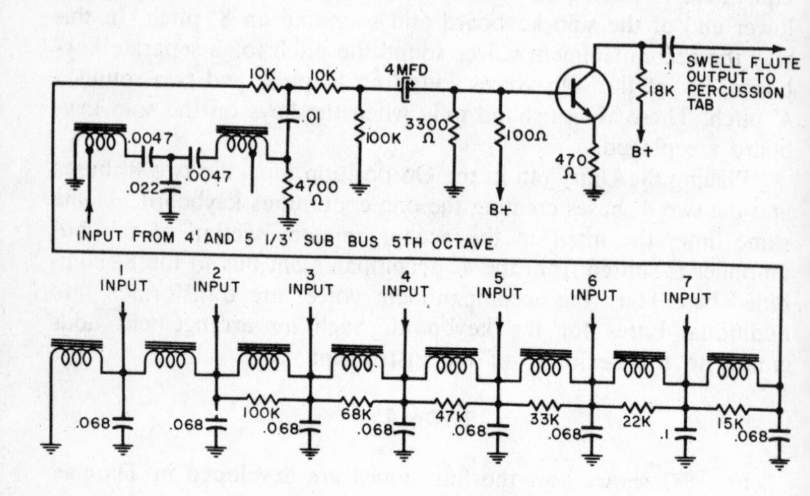

INPUT	FROM SUB BUS	
(1)	16'	3RD OCTAVE
	8'	2ND OCTAVE
(2)	16'	4TH OCTAVE
	8'	3RD OCTAVE
	5 1/3'	2ND OCTAVE
(3)	16'	4TH OCTAVE
	8'	3RD OCTAVE
	5 1/3'	3RD OCTAVE
	4'	2ND OCTAVE
(4)	16'	5TH OCTAVE
	8'	4TH OCTAVE
	5 1/3'	3RD OCTAVE
	4'	3RD OCTAVE
(5)	16'	5TH OCTAVE
	8'	4TH OCTAVE
	5 1/3'	4TH OCTAVE
	4'	3RD OCTAVE
(6)	8'	5TH OCTAVE
	5 1/3'	4TH OCTAVE
	4'	4TH OCTAVE
(7)	8'	5TH OCTAVE
	5 1/3'	5TH OCTAVE
	4'	4TH OCTAVE

Fig. 8-7. Thomas voicing circuit.

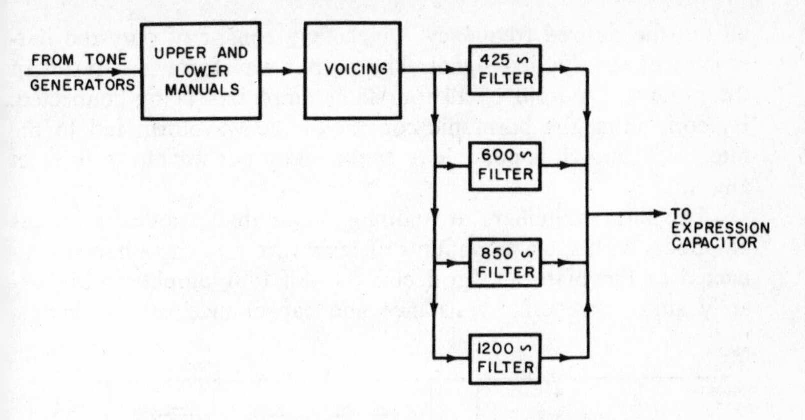

Fig. 8-8. Block diagram of Lowrey voicing system.

Voicing circuits in many models use identical waveshaping networks. Some slight difference may be found in component values but if the end results were to be placed side by side, no appreciable difference could be found.

LOWREY

The Lowrey Model LSA voicing circuit (Fig. 8-8) consists of a combination of R-C networks and special filter amplifiers.

The output signals from both upper and lower manuals are connected to basic waveshaping networks; Fig. 8-9 shows the switching arrangements and their associated R-C networks. The tab switch (represented by the shaded area) connects the signals to the filter-amplifier input in varied amounts of harmonic content because of the action of the R-C networks. The output signals from the voice and tab switch assembly are then connected simultaneously to all four filter amplifiers.

These amplifiers are designed to provide maximum gain at a specific frequency. Thus maximum attenuation is maintained to all but the desired frequency, which may consist of only the harmonics of the applied signal. The output waveform is a result of the input and output of all four filter amplifiers being connected. By controlling the harmonic content of the waveform fed to the filter amplifiers, it is possible to evoke an output waveform to meet any voice.

The filter amplifiers are nothing more than triode band-pass amplifiers with specific amounts of resistance and capacitance connected to the plate and grid circuits. All four amplifiers are exactly alike, except for resistance and capacitance values. In this

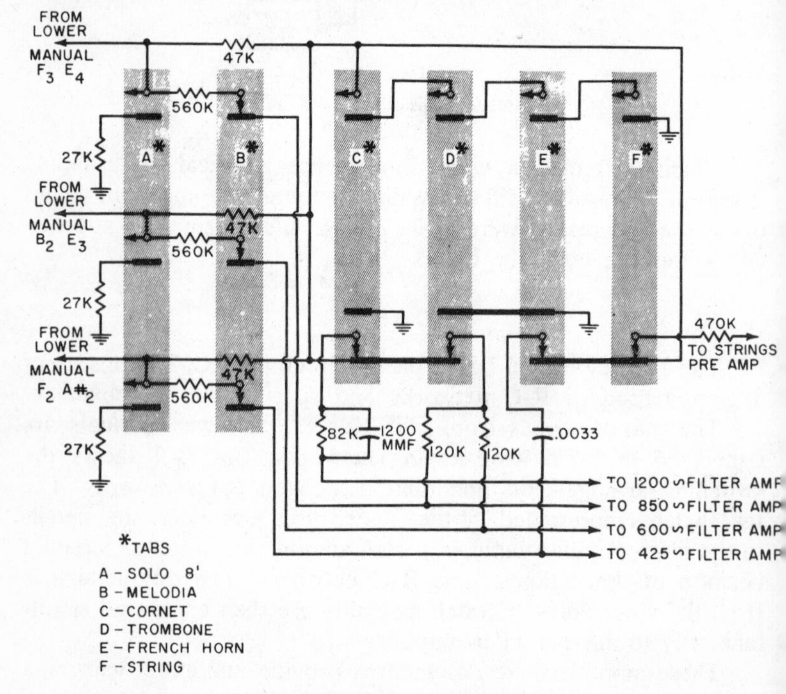

Fig. 8-9. Lowrey voicing tabs.

particular Lowrey Model, type 6SL7 tubes are utilized as filter amplifiers. Some models use more amplifiers than shown here, but the principle of operation is always the same.

The combined output from the filter amplifiers is fed to the expression control; to the main power amplifier; then to the speaker system.

PEDAL VOICING CIRCUITS

The pedal voicing circuits are also included in the voicing networks. They shape the waveform produced by the pedal generators. There is no difference between these and other voicing circuits, except for component values (frequency is handled by the pedal voicing circuits) and of course, the shape of the original waveform from the pedal generators.

The square pedal generator waveform is quite common because of the large number of organs which employ the Eccles-Jordan divider circuits constructed into a symmetrical multivibrator. In this case, the selection of filter components is somewhat different from the case of a sawtooth voltage waveform which may be generated by the main tone generator assembly.

OUTPHASE VOICES

A voicing arrangement that requires mention is that used to develop some of the reed instrument sounds *(outphase)*. Because of the timbre quality of reed instruments, (e.g., clarinet, oboe, and tibia) a special circuit arrangement is needed to imitate their voices.

The timbre quality of a tone changes with its harmonic structure. The even harmonic content in the emitted waveform of the reed instruments, however, is negligible. This unique characteristic necessitates a different approach to recreating the reed sound with the electronic organ.

Fig. 8-6 shows the block diagram of the bus amplifier arrangement in Kinsman Model A. The lowest block shows the 8′ outphaser bus amplifier, so named because of the bus amplifier connection.

Notice the signals applied at the outphaser bus-amplifier input consist of the 4′ bus amplifier output and the 8′ collecting bus-line signals—two signals with a frequency ratio of 2:1. This means the even harmonics of the 8′ tones are attenuated to some extent by the application of the 4′ tones on them. Thus the necessary harmonic content is such that the 8′ clarinet tones may be duplicated when this signal is passed through the clarinet voicing circuits.

To state it technically, an electrical wave without even harmonics is symmetrical above and below its baseline. The sawtooth waveform from the tone generators is made symmetrical by adding to the fundamental frequency a sawtooth tone an octave higher, halved in amplitude and reversed in phase.

CHAPTER 9

Amplifiers And Power Supplies

The audio amplifier and power supply are equally as important to the electronic organ as any of the circuitry previously described. The former accurately reproduces the full organ tonal quality put out by the tone generating system. Usually capable of excellent frequency ranges, it varies in audio-output power from 20 to as many as 50 watts. The power supply furnishes the necessary voltages to all circuits within the organ, and maintains critical tolerances to the voltage variations. In most cases, both amplifier and power supply are designed to meet the requirements of the remainder of the organ circuitry.

Voltage regulation is accomplished with voltage regulator circuits. When special transistor circuits are used, special attention must be given to the type of voltage regulation as well as tolerance in respect to voltage variations within the circuit.

MAGNAVOX

The Magnavox Model A-10 amplifier and power supply are shown in Fig. 9-1. In the amplifier system, the high and low frequencies are handled by separate amplifier channels, provided an excellent minimum-distortion audio signal to drive the speakers. Separation between the treble and bass frequencies is held at a maximum through this method amplification.

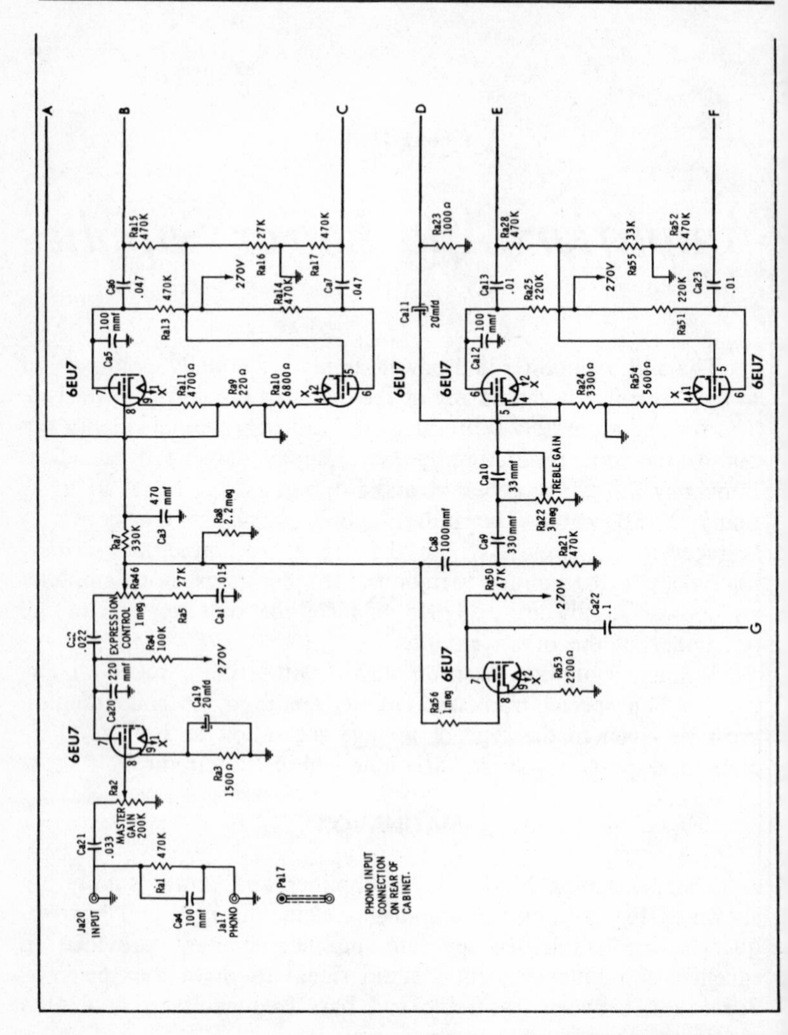

Fig. 9-1. Magnavox audio

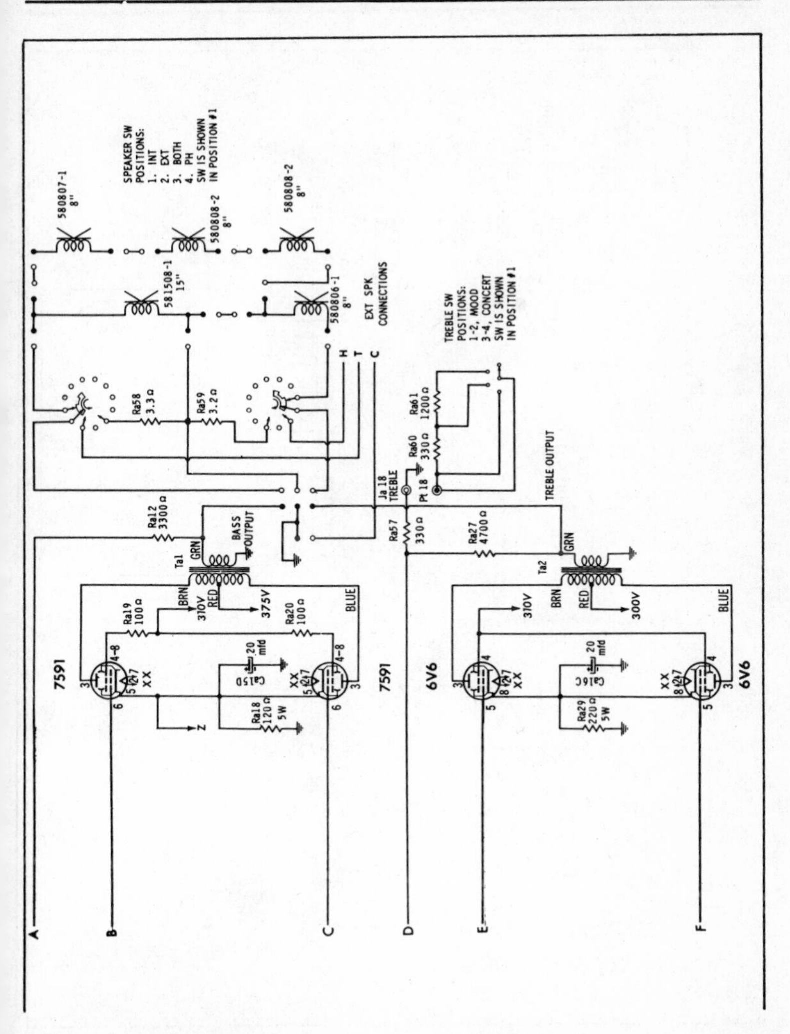

amplifier and power supply.

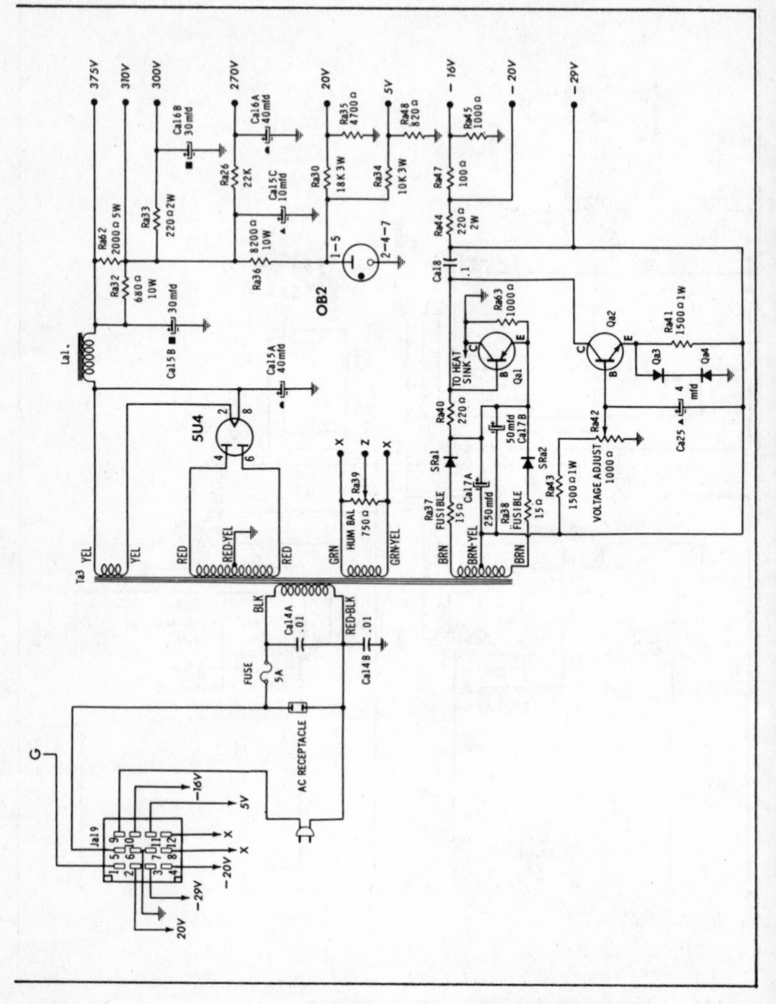
375V
310V
300V
270V
20V
5V
- 16V
- 20V
- 29V
Ca16B 30 mfd
Ca16A 40 mfd
Ra35 4700 Ω
Ra48 820 Ω
Ra45 1000 Ω
Ra26 22K
Ra30 18K 3W
Ra34 10K 3W
Ra47 100 Ω
Ca15C 10 mfd
Ra33 220 Ω 2W
Ra62 2000 Ω 5W
Ra44 220 Ω 2W
Ra36 8200 Ω 10W
1-5
2-4-7
OB2
Ca18 .1
Ra32 680 Ω 10W
Ca15B 30 mfd
Ra63 1000 Ω
Qa2
Ra41 1500 Ω 1W
La1
TO HEAT SINK
Qa1
Qa3
Qa4
Ca15A 40 mfd
Ca25 4 mfd
5U4
Ra40 220 Ω
50 mfd Ca17B
Ra42
X
Z
X
SRa1
SRa2
Ra39
HUM BAL 750 Ω
Ca17A 250 mfd
Ra37 FUSIBLE 15 Ω
Ra38 FUSIBLE 15 Ω
Ra43 1500 Ω 1W
VOLTAGE ADJUST 1000 Ω
Ta3
YEL
YEL
RED
RED-YEL
RED
GRN
GRN-YEL
BRN
BRN-YEL
BRN
BLK
RED-BLK
Ca14A .01
Ca14B .01
FUSE 5A
AC RECEPTACLE
G
Ja19
-16V
5V
X
X
-20V
-29V
20V

Fig. 9-1. (cont.)

The first voltage amplifier consists of a half a 6EU7 common to both bass and treble channels. The output signal from this stage is connected to the foot-operated expression control, which feeds it to the two channels.

Fig. 9-2 shows a rear view of the amplifier and expression pedal. Most electronic organs use a conventional audio amplifier —a standard type circuit with which every serviceman is familiar —with only minor circuit variations. The serviceman may be less familiar, with certain voltage regulator circuits.

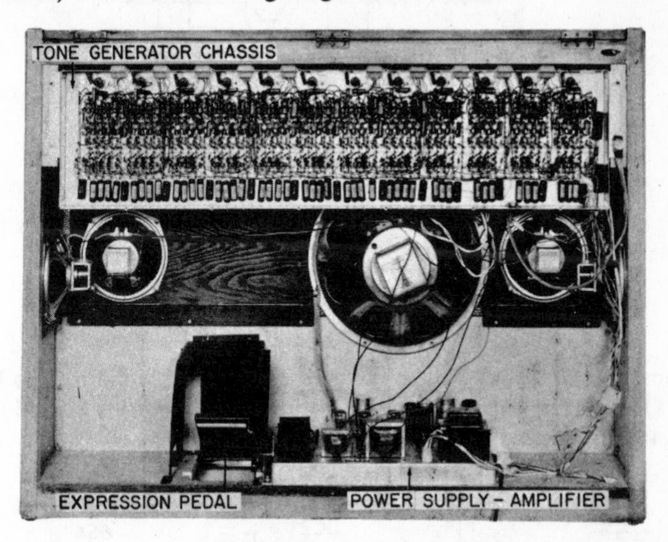

Courtesy Magnavox Company.

Fig. 9-2. Rear view of Magnavox organ.

The Model A-10 power supply utilizes a full-wave vacuum tube rectifier to supply the B+ voltage required for operation of the amplifier. Other B+ voltages are obtained through the voltage-divider networks with the outputs regulated by the OB2 voltage-regulator tube.

The negative source, which supplies a regulated voltage to insure proper operation of the transistor circuits, requires special mention. Note in Fig. 9-3 the two silicon rectifiers providing full wave rectification are connected across the secondary of the power transformer Ta3. The negative voltage is taken from the center tap of the transformer winding. The output voltage is regulated by

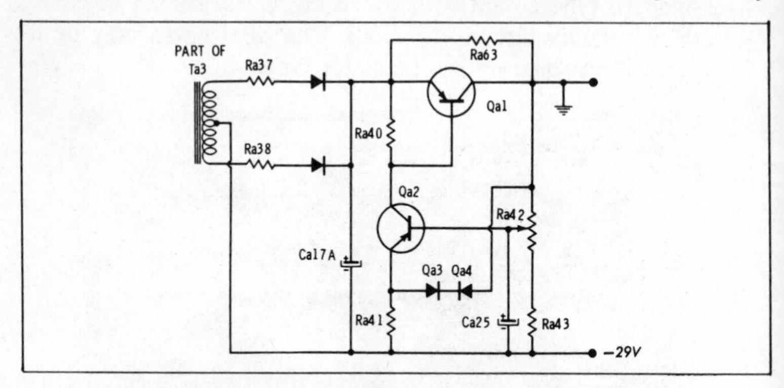

Fig. 9-3. Magnavox regulator circuit.

transistors Qa1 and Qa2, connected as a series regulator. The base of Qa1 will be slightly negative with respect to the emitter due to Ra40, thus providing forward bias. The emitter of Qa2 is con-

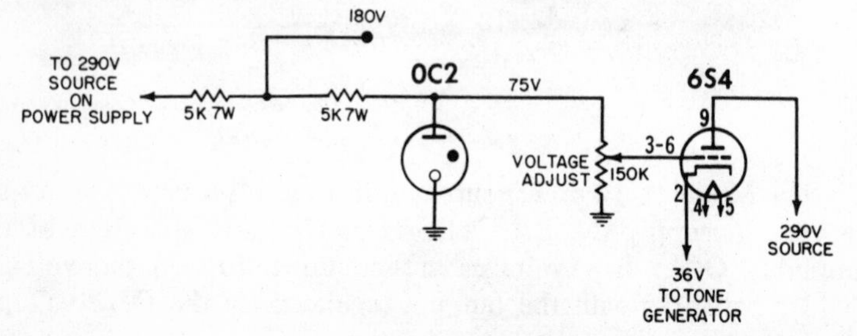

Fig. 9-4. Conn regulator circuit.

nected to the negative source through Ra41. Connected to the Qa2 emitter is a zener diode, Qa3, and a protection diode, Qa4, which provide a voltage reference level for the Qa2 emitter.

Variations appear as a voltage change at the base of Qa2 through Ra43 and adjustable control Ra42. Since the voltage at the emitter is stabilized by the zener diodes, the voltage change at the base of Qa2 causes more or less current to flow between the base and emitter. An amplified signal appears at the collector of

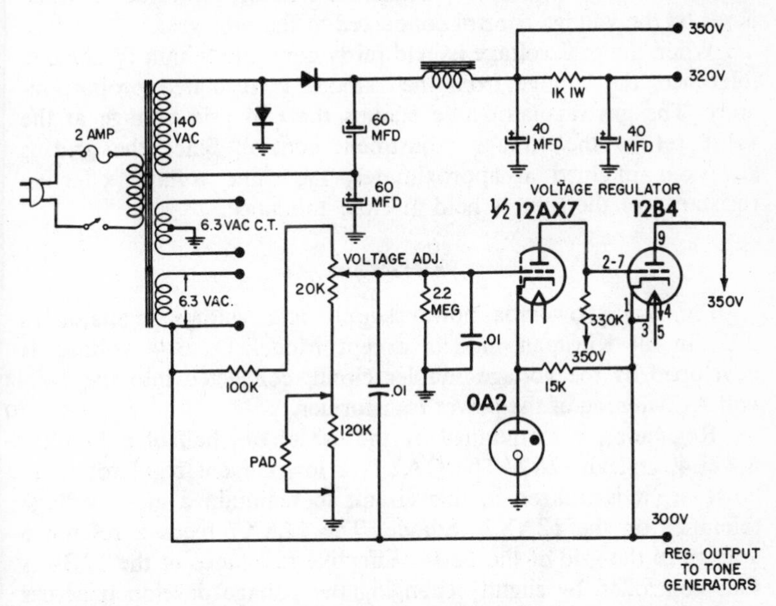

Fig. 9-5. Kinsman power supply and regulator.

Qa2 and the base of Qa1. This controls the current through Qa1, maintaining a constant output voltage.

CONN GENERATOR REGULATOR

The method used in the Conn Model 540 to control the voltage for the tone-generator plates is shown in the simplified schematic, Fig. 9-4.

A 6S4 triode establishes the voltage on the tone-generator plates. Voltage is varied by adjusting the grid voltage, thereby controlling current through the tube. In effect, the 6S4 appears to its load (tone generators) as a variable resistor, the value of which is set by the voltage control connected to the tube grid.

When the grid voltage is held fairly constant, within reasonable tolerance, the voltage from the cathode is regulated proportionately. The gas regulator-tube clamps the 6S4 grid voltage at the value set by the voltage adjustment control. Since the grid is always maintained at approximately the same voltage, effective resistance of the tube is held at close tolerance.

KINSMAN

Fig. 9-5 shows the power supply and voltage regulator as used in all Kinsman models except Model D. B+ voltage is developed by the voltage-doubler circuit connected into the 140-volt AC winding of the power transformer.

Regulation is maintained by the use of one-half of a 12AX7, a 12B4, and an OA2. The OA2 is a low current regulator tube; however, it is utilized in this circuit to maintain a close voltage tolerance on the 12AX7 cathode. The 12AX7 feeds a reference voltage to the grid of the 12B4. Effective resistance of the 12B4 is thus controlled by slightly changing the voltage developed across the 300-volt B+ line. Any voltage deviation that occurs on the 300-volt line is immediately corrected, because: a voltage change on the 12AX7 grid results in a voltage change in the 12B4 grid circuit; this in turn changes the current through the 12B4 and corrects the voltage deviation.

By connecting a voltage regulator in this fashion, the low-current OA2 is used to control a rather high-current triode, 12B4, thus providing regulation to all tone generators within the instrument.

EXPRESSION CONTROLS

The Expression control, mentioned several times during the discussion of other circuits within the electronic organ, is a foot

Courtesy Conn Organ Corporation.

Fig. 9-6. Conn expression control.

pedal used, in all models discussed here, to control the audio output volume from the speaker system.

Like other functions in electronic organs, the Expression control circuitry may take many different forms. No matter which

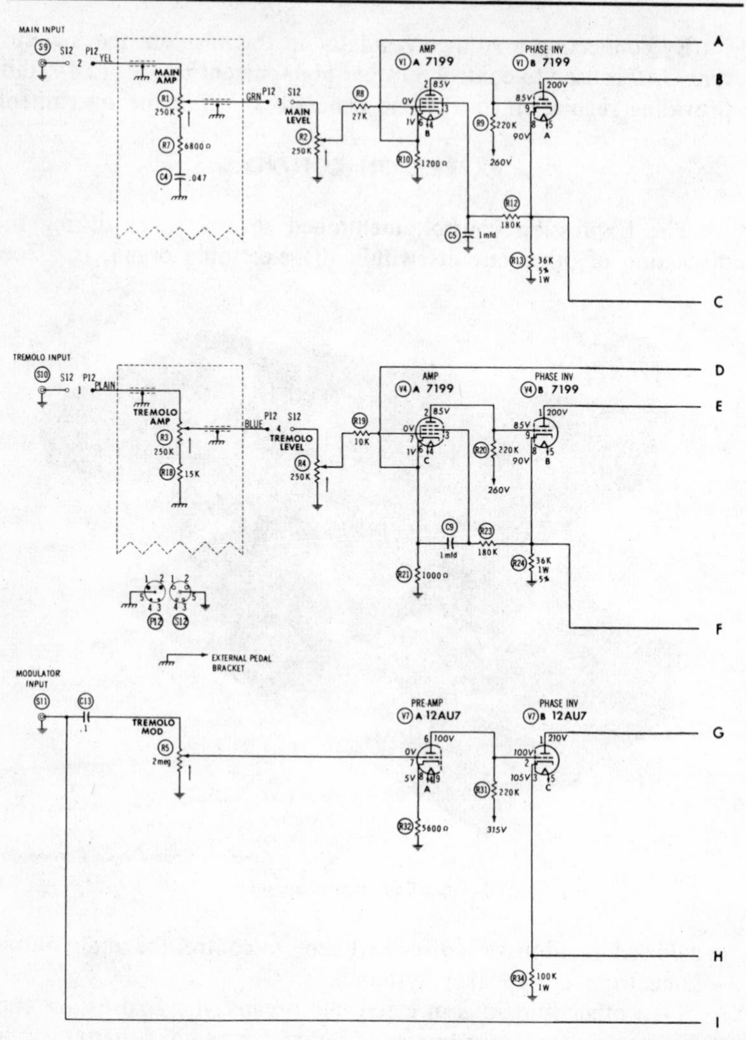
MAIN INPUT
TREMOLO INPUT
MODULATOR INPUT
MAIN AMP
TREMOLO AMP
MAIN LEVEL
TREMOLO LEVEL
TREMOLO MOD
AMP
PHASE INV
PRE-AMP
V1 A 7199
V1 B 7199
V4 A 7199
V4 B 7199
V7 A 12AU7
V7 B 12AU7
EXTERNAL PEDAL BRACKET
A
B
C
D
E
F
G
H
I

Fig. 9-7. Conn

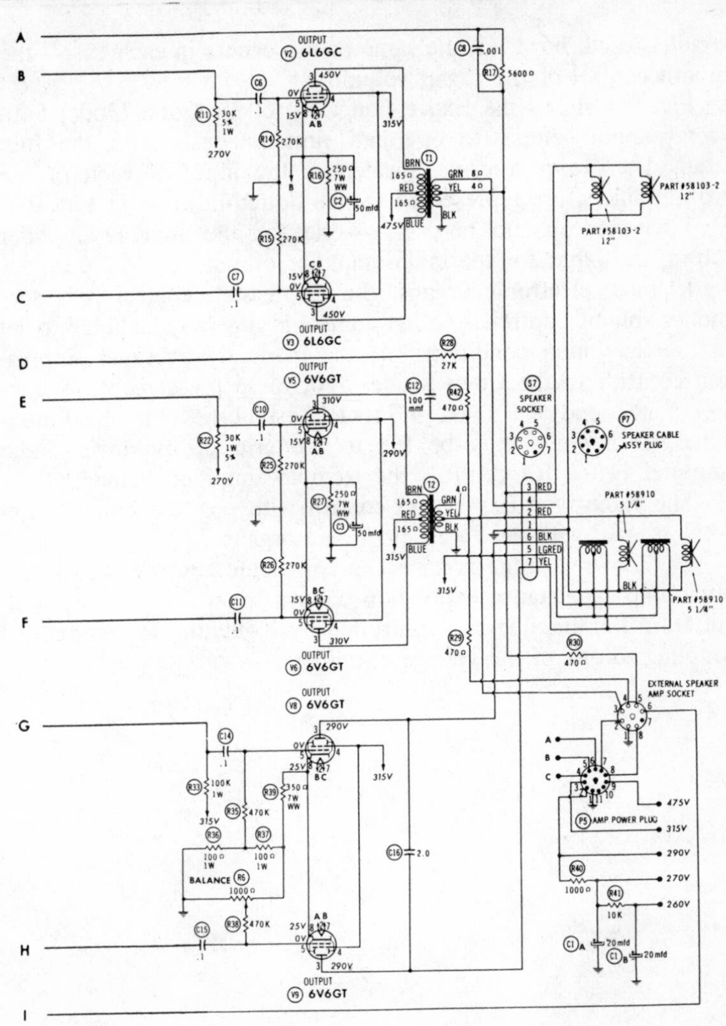

audio amplifiers.

circuit is used, however, the same action occurs in each case—the smooth control of the organ volume.

Fig. 9-6 shows the Expression Control for Conn Model 540. Two potentiometers are operated simultaneously with the foot pedal. These two controls, located at the input of each of the two amplifiers, are represented by the dotted-in areas in Fig. 9-7.

Two controls are necessary—one for the tremolo-amplifier output, the other for the main-amplifier output.

In most electronic organs, the Expression control is a secondary volume control. Another control is generally included to set up the maximum conditions for the manually operated Expression control. In the Conn Model 540, these preset controls consist of R2 and R4 (Fig. 9-7). R2 establishes the maximum-signal level which may be fed to the grid of the main audio amplifier, while R4 controls the tremolo-amplifier channel.

The same type Expression control with possible minor variations, is used with nearly all electronic organs.

The Lowrey organ is an exception. Some Lowrey models use a variable capacitance expression control, in which the final output from the amplifiers is controlled by regulating the amount of coupling to one of the voltage amplifiers.

CHAPTER 10

Tuning And Adjustment Procedures

Faulty tuning or adjustment of an electronic organ can cause irreparable damage to certain parts of the instrument. An improperly set transistor bias control, for example, may ruin a large number of transistors.

The serviceman should try, if at all possible, to obtain information directly from the manufacturer of the particular instrument with which he is concerned. Having this information at hand will help insure proper maintenance and result in better customer relations.

In most cases the manufacturer will co-operate in supplying the technician with the necessary servicing information (often in the form of a service manual). Some manuals contain all the necessary information for complete set-up adjustments as well as a complete tuningprocedure. Occasionally, however, this manual contains only schematics and basic theory of major circuit operation.

The manufacturer is equally as interested in efficient repair and maintenance for his product as is the serviceman. A poor repair job could result in an unsatisfied customer with an unfavorable reflection on the quality of a particular model.

The chart in this chapter is for general use and not designed for any particular instrument. Although all organs operate basically alike, each has its own pecularities which must be taken into consideration before tuning and adjustment procedure can be determined.

GENERAL ORGAN CHECKOUT PROCEDURE

Following is the suggested checking procedure, for use in installation and before troubleshooting. It is further suggested that the procedure be followed in sequence.

1. Plug in the organ and turn on the power switch. Make certain the pilot light is on.
2. Place all voice tabs in the Off position. Return all control tabs to their normal positions.
3. Depress one solo voice tab and make certain each solo manual key sounds. Depress the Vibrato tab to see that vibrato is present at all keys on the keyboard. With one key down, depress the Vibrato Full switch. This should increase the vibrato. Return all tabs to the Off position.
4. Depress each Solo Voice tab on the solo manual individually. Make certain that each key sounds. Depress the Expression pedal to check for smooth control of the volume level. Return all solo voice tabs to the Off positions.
5. Depress the 4′ Voice tabs on the accompaniment manual. Make certain each note sounds on the lower manual.
6. Depress two voice tabs on the 8′ accompaniment. Check each note on the accompaniment manual for proper function. Return the 8′ accompaniment tabs to the Off position.
7. Depress the Solo Sustain, the Flute 8′, and the Diapason tabs. Check each note on the solo manual for proper functioning of sustain. Return all control and voice tabs to the Off position.
8. Depress one voice tab. Check each note on the pedalboard for proper operation. Depress the Pedal Sustain tab and one foot pedal, and check for proper pedal sustain. Return all controls to the Off position.
9. While holding one or more notes, check each tab on the solo manual for proper operation of voicing filter and switch.

10. Repeat 9 for the accompaniment manual.
11. Repeat 9 for the pedal voices.
12. Depress all voicing tabs and strike a large chord-near the bottom of both solo and accompaniment manuals. At the same time, depress a pedal note. Check for power handling ability or breakup of the tones.

The list is necessarily incomplete: it would be impossible to enumerate all the repair problems which are encountered in the electronic organ. For this reason, it is important that the technician gain a thorough general knowledge of how the organ works, so that when called on to do so, he can make his own diagnosis and put the instrument back into working condition with a minimum of delay.

Certain alien sounds are corollary to particular normal conditions in the electronic organ, and should not be mistaken for symptoms of defectiveness. With the preset volume control turned on full, the expression pedal open, and no keys being played, a humming noise sometimes emanates from the organ. If the instrument is played within the confines of a room, the noise will be quite apparent; adjust the present level control properly and it will no longer be bothersome. Also in a quiet room with the volume up, feedthrough may be heard from one manual when played with no tabs depressed. This fault is merely theoretical, however, since there would be no point in playing a manual without tabs. It is possible to make meaningless tests and discover theoretical faults.

Example: The organ hums loudly when turned on. First, operate the expression pedal; if moving the pedal affects the volume of the hum, it obviously is coming through the Expression Control and cannot be originating in the output stages of the amplifier. Next, check the top volume control on the amplifier and amplifier input. If these both affect the hum, the first intermediate and input stages of the amplifier have been eliminated. But it is simpler to proceed to the tabs.

CHART 10-1.

Trouble chart for a typical electronic organ.

Symptom	Cause	Remedy
All stops of one footage dead or very weak.	Defective bus-amplifier tube or circuit, or connector on bus-amplifier assembly loose or pulled off.	Check connectors first; if O.K., replace tube. Replace bus-amplifier assembly, if necessary.
One stop dead, other stops of same footage function normally.	Defective voicing assembly, probably switch or through-connecting eyelet.	Inspect voicing assembly. If not easily corrected, replace assembly or write factory for instructions
Loud hum when stops of one footage are on; especially full-bodied stops.	Defective bus-amplifier stage; probably heater-cathode leakage in bus amplifier tube.	Replace tube. Replace bus-amplifier assembly, if necessary.
One note dead in all positions on one keyboard, but other octaves of same note function normally.	Output connector at tone-generator assembly loose or pulled off.	Replace connector.
Same as above, but dead or intermittent note on one position only, on one keyboard; other positions of same note function normally.	Defect in keyboard, broken connection or bent switch contact.	This fault, which occurs very rarely, requires accurate service; if it is to be corrected without replacing the entire keyboard. Consult factory for instructions.

CHART 10-1. (Continued)

Trouble chart for a typical electronic organ.

Symptom	Cause	Remedy
Bad note, rough or choppy sounding, or way-off pitch. May be worse with full or almost full vibrato. Lower octaves of same note also bad, but top octave functions normally.	Tone-generator frequency-divider stage out of synchronism.	Replace tone-generator tube or complete assembly.
Same as above, but top octave is also bad or dead.	Defective master-oscillator stage in tone generator.	Replace master-oscillator tube. Replace tone-generator assembly, if changing tube does not correct fault.
Note scratchy when key is depressed. In an extreme case this may be confused with a bad note, except that it occurs on one keyboard position only.	Dirty keyswitch contact.	Usually can be cleared by operating key rapidly several times. In stubborn cases, consult factory for instruction on cleaning contact buses (Such cleaning should be attempted only by a qualified service technician).
Console rattles. Sometimes a rattle is induced by notes of a particular pitch and is mistaken for a bad note; but it usually appears on two or	Loose part in console. For instance, one of the screws holding the treble speakers might be loose enough so its lockwasher rattles.	Find rattle and tighten loose part.

CHART 10-1. (Continued)

Trouble chart for a typical electronic organ.

Symptom	**Cause**	**Remedy**
three adjacent notes, and tends to clear up as volume is reduced.		
All pedal notes from any one note to top of pedal keyboard, dead.	Defective contact on highest operating pedal keyswitch.	Check to see if power cord loop (or edge of deep carpet, etc.) is caught under back of pedal keyboard and partially depressing one or more pedals. If necessary, dismount pedal keyboard and inspect contacts.
Pedal 16′ voices sound at 8′ pitch.	Pedal frequency divider inoperative, or 16′ pedal-generator output disconnected.	Change pedal frequency-divider tube. Check connections. Replace circuit assembly, including pedal generator, if necessary.
No vibrato.	Defective vibrato-oscillator tube, or vibrato-oscillator component.	Change tube. If this does not correct fault, trace path of vibrato signal, using service manual if available.

Next, turn off all the tabs; if the hum stops, the entire amplifier and part of the voicing panel circuitry have been eliminated. Now turn on the tabs, one at a time. The hum may reappear only with certain tabs. Suppose it is heard when one or more of the lower-keyboard tabs is on; then the fault is in some part of the organ common to these tabs and no others. The most likely place is the 8′ lower-keyboard section of the bus amplifier; and the component most likely to be at fault is a tube. Locate the offending tube on the bus-amplifier panel by replacing the tubes one at a time.

Example: A faulty note is encountered; i.e., the note sputters, warbles, or is badly off pitch. Almost certainly the trouble is in the tone generator for that note. To verify this suspicion, return to the tabs. Listen to the note, using one tab at a time. Remember that each note appears in several places on the two keyboards, and has a separate tab for each; if the fault is in the generator, the defective sound will be heard in all these positions. Or by changing from an 8′ to a 4′ tab while moving down an octave on the keyboard, the same generated note may be heard again.

It is important to remember the frequency divider failure. Remember that each note is derived, in the tone generator, from the note an octave above it. Therefore, frequency divider stage failure will manifest itself as a faulty note—faulty not only at one particular pitch, but throughout all octaves.

It must be determined whether the fault originates in the master oscillator at the head of the chain, where it is often corrected by simply replacing a tube, or in a later stage, where it calls for replacement of the entire generator assembly for that particular note.

Turn on the upper-manual 4′ Flute tab and listen to the offending note in the top octave. If it is dead or radically off pitch, the trouble is in the master oscillator. If the top octave is functioning properly, the fault resides in a later stage, and it will be necessary to replace the generator assembly.

Example: A pedal note is malfunctioning or completely dead. First, check whether a loop of the power cord is caught under the back of the pedal keyboard depressing the pedal slightly. If not, listen to the same note in the lowest octave on the manual keyboard. If the fault is also present there, the tone generator for that note must be replaced. Barring these two problems the trouble may be simply a loose connector at the bottom of the tone generator panel.

Do not be misled by secondary symptoms which may arise from a fault. For instance, suppose the 4′ upper-manual output from the bus amplifier becomes disconnected. Of course the 4′ tabs go dead; and if they are tried one at a time, the trouble is quickly discovered. But suppose the test is not carried out; instead, the investigator becomes aware of the following secondary symptom: With no tabs on at all, a rather weak 4′ signal, stringlike in tone color, is heard. With 8′ or 16′ full-bodied tabs (flute, etc.), this stringlike tone noticeably alters the 8′ and 16′ tone color. The point is that if the investigator follows this line of thought, he may easily be led away from the real solution to the problem.

Trouble Chart 10-1 lists some typical electronic organ defects and their remedies.

TUNING

Equipment for tuning the electronic organ ranges from the tuning fork to elaborate and costly electronic equipment. In the following discussion, an effort is made to place at the technician's disposal a practical and inexpensive method of tuning almost any electronic organ. The experienced technician may find that all that is necessary is a single tuning fork. However, for precise tuning, it may be necessary to use a commercially constructed unit.

Preliminary Tuning

The electronic organ is tuned simply by placing each tone-generating device on the correct frequency with respect to its corresponding key. To do this, it is necessary to establish a reference frequency from which to tune. The standard reference frequency must be correctly pitched and fall within the range of the organ. A properly tuned piano offers a handy reference.

No matter what method is employed, tuning information (usually available only from the manufacturer) will be

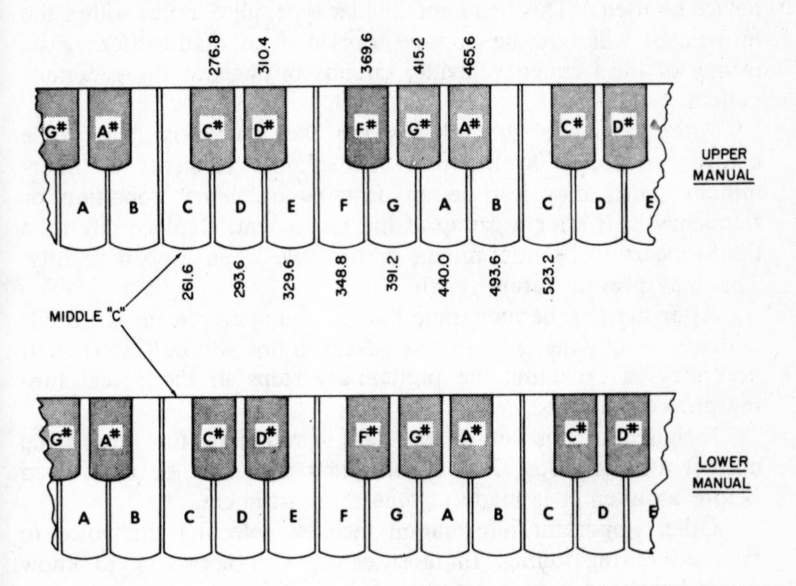

Fig. 10-1. Middle octave frequency diagram.

(Note: During tuning, be sure to use the correct octave to correspond to the available tuning forks.)

Table 10-1 shows only the middle octave, which contains Middle *C*. With the Middle *C* tuning fork as reference (261.6 cps), place Middle *C* on its correct operating frequency.

Grasp the tuning fork firmly and force it into vibration by striking it against the heel of your shoe. Depress Middle *C* on the organ keyboard and tune the *C* master oscillator to "zero" beat (no difference in frequency) with the tuning fork.

In most cases, it is necessary to tune the master-oscillator coil. (In these instances, it is recommended that a non-metallic tuning device be used.) This being the divider type, all *C* notes within the instrument will now be in tune, provided no malfunctions exist in any of the frequency divider circuits throughout the generator system.

After tuning a note always tap the master-oscillator tube before proceeding to the next note. Loose elements or intermittent shorts may lead to an unstable frequency condition or frequency drift after warmup of the instrument. Replace any tube that appears to be intermittent or unstable when tapped slightly. This may prevent future repairs.

After the *C* generator, tune the remaining eleven master oscillators in exactly the same manner. Next in line will be *C#, D, D#,* necessary in executing the preliminary steps to the actual tuning procedure.

Included in this information are instructions for setting the correct footage stops. This is important and *must* be considered before an attempt is made to tune the instrument.

Other important information includes selecting the voice to be used during tuning. In most cases, it is necessary to know which keyboard is to be employed.

Before tuning, also be sure the Vibrato and Tremolo tabs are in the Off position; because in some cases vibrato makes it difficult to determine when the instrument is in tune.

Tuning Procedure

As mentioned in Chapter 2 there are two types of tone-generating systems: the divider type and the individual tone generator type. Of the two the former is the easier to tune. Only twelve adjustments are necessary—one to place each master oscillator on its correct frequency. When this is done, all succeeding notes of the same character are automatically in tune. For example, when the *C* master-oscillator is tuned, all *C* notes fall into the correct frequency.

The latter type is tuned in the same manner; but considerably more work is involved since there is a separate oscillator for every note in the keyboard. It is only necessary to keep in mind the type of generator system to be tuned, and then follow the tuning procedure accordingly.

Tuning Fork Method

Tuning may be accomplished in several ways. One is with the tuning fork. The service technician may use a fork for each frequency as shown in Fig. 10-1. In this case, each master oscillator in the divider system is placed on its correct frequency by using the proper tuning fork as a reference.

Consult the service manual, if available, for the model to be tuned, and carry out the preliminary steps: set tabs correctly, establish necessary special voltages, etc. The tuning procedure may now be started.

First, establish the reference point for the tuning process. This may be done by locating Middle *C*, as shown in Table 10-1. Middle *C* on the organ manual is the *C* nearest the center of each manual keyboard.

To find Middle *C* on the lower manual (Fig. 10-1), be seated at the organ and locate the *C* just to the left of the organ center. Middle *C* on the upper manual will be found directly above Middle *C* on the lower manual. All tuning must be done on the upper manual.
and so on until all twelve notes in the middle octave have been properly tuned.

For the individual tone-generator system, use the tuning forks to tune one octave on the keyboard. That octave may then be used as a reference for the others. This is a tricky procedure, however, and should be attempted only by experienced technicians.

Table 10.1. Tuning procedure.

Referring to Fig. 10-1 as a guide, select a standard frequency reference (C 261.6 thru C 523.2). The following steps use C above Middle C for a reference as an example. (Beats referred to in the steps are counted in 10 seconds.)

Step	Depress Key	Adjust Master Oscillator
1	C above Middle C;	C to "zero" beat.
2	Middle C and G simultaneously;	G to 10 beats.
3	G and D simultaneously;	D to 14 beats.
4	D and A simultaneously;	A to 10 beats.
5	A and E simultaneously;	E to 14 beats.
6	E and B simultaneously;	B to 10 beats.
7	B and F# simultaneously;	F# to 14 beats.
8	F# and C# simultaneously;	C# to 14 beats.
9	C# and G# simultaneously;	G# to 10 beats.
10	G# and D# simultaneously;	D# to 14 beats.
11	D# and A# simultaneously;	A# to 10 beats.
12	A# and F simultaneously;	F to 14 beats
13	F and C above Middle C;	if 10 beats is not apparent, repeat each step.

NOTE: DO NOT ADJUST C ABOVE MIDDLE C AS A MEASURE OF CORRECTION TO 10 BEATS.

Tuning with one fork—The divider tone-generating system may be tuned using a single fork; if only one is available. This is, however, a time-consuming method, and more critical attention must be given to tuning practices. As previously mentioned always refer to the service manual, when available, for special tuning instructions on the specific model.

Table 10-1 shows the procedure to be followed for correct tuning by this method. Some practice may be necessary to use this chart properly.

Electronic Tuning Devices

Use of the electronic devices probably results in the most accurate tuning. Several such instruments are manufactured commercially; among them are the Conn Strobotuner and Stroboconn. These are nothing more than counting devices, similar to the strobodisc used to check turntable speeds of a phonograph. The Strobotuner in fact, has a built-in strobodisc driven at a constant speed by a synchronous motor.

The disc has light and dark areas in staggered intervals over its entire surface (Fig. 10-2). Directly behind it are neon lamps used to illuminate the lighter portions of the scanning disc.

Courtesy Conn Organ Corporation.

Fig. 10-2. Strobotuner disc.

The firing rate of the neon lamps is determined by the frequency applied to the Strobotuner via a microphone or patch cord from an external jack on the organ.

Thus, the frequency rate of the input signal may be compared to the synchronous running rate of the strobodisc variations. As the scanning disc revolves, the neon lamps are excited by the organ signal and an area corresponding to the frequency is seen on the scanning disc. If both disc and signal are on the same frequency, the corresponding portion of the scanning disc will appear to be stationary. Otherwise, the disc will appear to move at a rate dependent on the difference between the two frequencies.

Another electronic tuning device is the Peterson Chromatic Tuner Model 200. This instrument supplies 72 highly accurate standard organ pitches. The organ tones are beat, one at a time, against their corresponding tuner pitches, and at the same time adjusted until the beat disappears. The beat will be quite audible unless the two tones sounding together are of the same pitch.

Electronic tuning instruments may be used on any model organ, but are especially effective on models using individual generators for each note, since their frequency range is wide enough to include the entire organ keyboard.

CHAPTER 11

Accessories

Among the accessories available for the electronic organ are percussion units, chimes, bells, and special speaker units. Percussion is in many cases optional, rather than being an integral part of the organ (see Chapter 6).

LESLIE SPEAKER UNITS

One of the most popular speaker units today is the Leslie speaker unit, manufactured by Electro Music Company. There is a Leslie model made for nearly every organ in current production. Differences between these models are slight; often only in the interconnecting cables used for the organ hookup.

Models 45 and 47 are typical Leslie units: all other Leslie models are the same, except for variations in organ connections. These speaker cabinets are designed and equipped for use with Kinsman, Lowrey, Thomas, and Wurlitzer organs. Two controls are furnished: a switch for turning the tremolo on and off, and a speaker selector switch which permits the organist to use either the Leslie speaker (Echo), or the organ speaker system (Main), or both together (Ensemble).

The Model 45 cabinet (Fig. 11-1) is designed for the spinet organ. The Model 47 cabinet is intended for larger organs; its size permits better reproduction of the 16′ pedal tones generated by these instruments. The Model 47 utilizes the type 47 amplifier, which provides 40 watts of audio power.

Although the Model 45 speaker is normally equipped with the same amplifier as the 47; it may be obtained without the amplifier, in which case it derives its power from the console amplifier.

Amplifier and Electrical Maintenance

Replacement transformers, filter chokes, and tremolo relays are obtained from the Electro Music Company factory; standard

Courtesy Electro-Music Company.

Fig. 11-1. Leslie Model 45.

parts such as fuses, sockets, resistors, and capacitors may be obtained from most radio parts stores.

The amplifier is removed by taking out: first, the screw that holds its front end to the bottom of the cabinet; then the two motor plugs and speaker plugs. When replacing the amplifier, introduce the back end of the chassis into the cabinet so the amplifier guide and hold-down clamp engage the amplifier.

The amplifier uses a replaceable Slo-Blo 1½-ampere fuse to protect the power supply against short circuits.

Before replacing a blown fuse, determine the cause of fuse failure. Do not use a fuse of higher then specified current rating.

To achieve maximum power output for total power consumed, the amplifier uses a relatively simple regulating circuit to hold the output-tube screens at the best operating voltage, regardless of signal level variation (Fig. 11-2).

Gas-regulator tubes maintain a constant voltage drop (within rated limits) regardless of current variations. By choosing the proper gas tube, relative to the power-supply voltage, a closely held voltage is made available to the screens.

Distorted sound is often caused by an excessive volume-control setting. Amplifier gain is purposely greater than necessary, to enable low-output consoles to provide full sound power output. Arbitrary setting of the volume control at maximum results in distortion when the organ swell control is fully opened. The volume control should be set for maximum undistorted output.

If the amplifier is operating unsatisfactorily, and the trouble cannot be remedied by tube or electrolytic capacitor replacements, various voltages should be measured. If an abnormally high or low voltage is noted, it usually indicates a defective part in the associated circuit.

If the output transformer is replaced, the wire colors must be noted and the new transformer wired with the same color identification; otherwise the feedback circuit will cause oscillation. In the 47 power amplifier, this may be corrected by reversing the secondary leads where they are attached to the speaker socket (do not disturb the ground or feedback loop connections). The

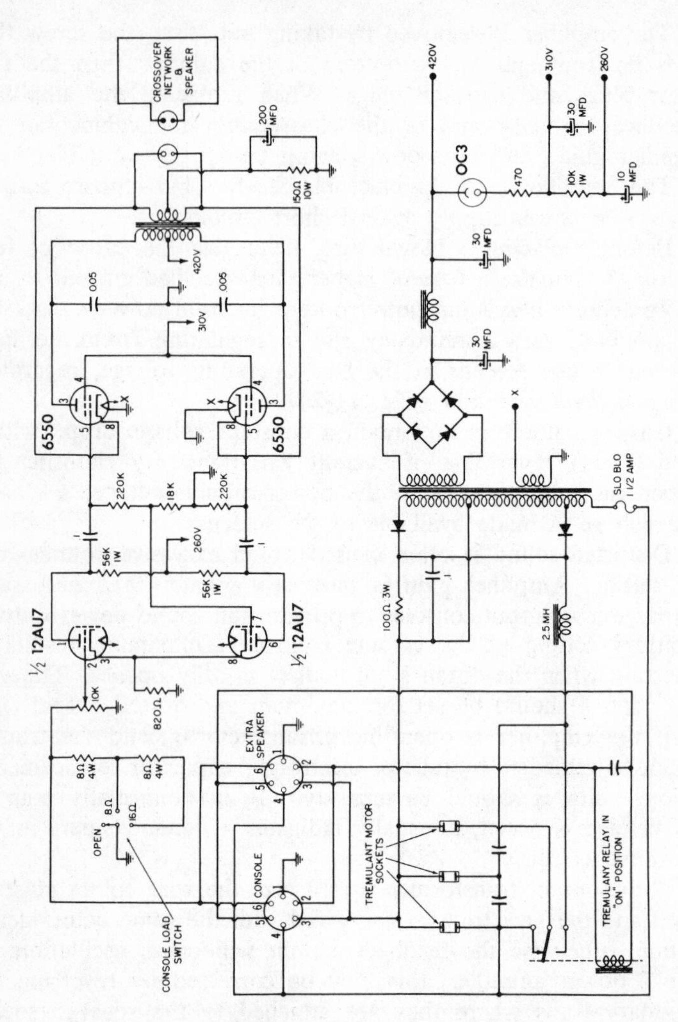

Fig. 11-2. Leslie amplifier.

output transformer-plate lead wires should be as short as possible and dressed close to the chassis.

Tubes are a common source of amplifier difficulty; although at times certain malfunctions, which appear to be caused by tubes, are actually the result of other conditions.

Most tube replacements may be obtained locally; for best operating results, however, the 6550 power tubes should be replaced with a matched pair.

Exceptionally low- or high-line voltage may cause difficulty with amplifier operation. If the line voltage falls below 100 volts, unsatisfactory performance will result. Low-line voltage may be caused by poor contacts at the cable connections, or by exceptionally long cable runs.

When the Model 45 speaker is not equipped with the type 47 amplifier, it must be equipped with a connector unit (Fig. 11-3). An important fuction of the connector unit is tremolo control. The relay in the connector unit supplies AC power to the tremulant motors (drive motors for the mechanical tremolo), when it is in the On position, and applies DC braking voltage when in the Off position.

The connector unit is easily removed from the Model 45 cabinet. First, remove the connecting cable and all plugs; next, remove the two mounting screws which secure the connector chassis to the bottom of the speaker cabinet, then the entire connector unit may be extracted.

When the tremolo control switch is in the Off position, braking is affected by applying, with the control relay, a direct current to the tremulant motors. (This current will do no harm since it is substantially below normal running rate.)

When the type 47 amplifier is used, DC braking voltage is obtained by means of taps on the power transformer primary and a full-wave rectifier circuit; and when the amplifier is omitted, an autoformer is substituted. Fusing for the latter unit is provided by a No. 47 lamp.

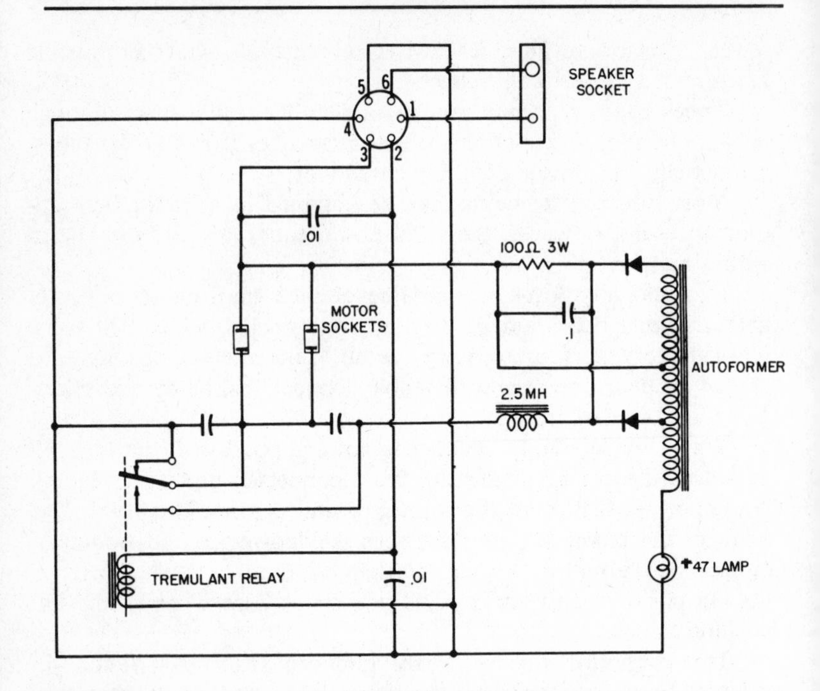

Fig. 11-3. Leslie cabinet connector.

The brake assembly is identical for both types. In replacing diodes, or assemblies containing diodes (brake or rectifier assemblies), soldering must be done very carefully: diodes, like transistors, are delicate components and may be injured by excessive heat.

Speaker System and Dividing Network

The Leslie unit uses a two-way system with separate speakers. Pedal and mid-range tones are generated by a heavy-duty 15-inch permanent-magnet speaker with nominal impedance of 16 ohms.

The upper middle and higher tones are generated by a compression sound-chamber driver unit, also with a permanent magnet and nominal impedance of 16 ohms.

The 15-inch speaker is mounted in a matched bass-reflex enclosure; therefore the cabinet back must be securely fastened in place. The high-frequency driver is loaded by means of a rotary horn. One horn in the upper rotor radiates sound; the other dynamically balances the assembly to eliminate vibration during rotation. A small cotton acoustic and dust filter is placed in the throat of the horn.

The two specialized-range speakers are connected to the amplifier via a two half-section *M*-derived frequency-dividing network (crossover), which electrically separates the bass and treble range amplifier outputs and directs the proper signal to each speaker. The nominal separation occurs at 800 cps. The impedances used in the loudspeaker system provide for a dividing network of extremely rugged and electrically stable parts. Trouble is seldom, if ever, encountered with this unit.

Mechanical Maintenance

After several years service, tremulant motors sometimes accumulate enough lint and dust to hamper ventilation and lubrication. This may be prevented, and motor life thus extended, by removing the motors periodically and cleaning them with solvent.

To remove and replace the upper motor, remove the motor power plug from the socket, and the two wing nuts. *Important:* The upper motor must run counterclockwise as viewed from the top or pulley end; otherwise, the upper tremulant rotor will not come up to speed. If the motor is disassembled or another motor substituted, always check for counterclockwise rotation.

To remove and replace the lower motor, follow the same procedure as above. When replacing, position the belt on the motor pulley before it is lifted into place on the mounting screws. Pull the front wing nut (which controls the tremulant drive-belt tension) to the left until the belt is tight; release and the belt will assume its proper tension. Tighten the wing nut at this position. Do not attempt to stretch the belt tight and hold it with the wing nut: too much tension creates noise and makes the motor hard to start.

If the motor is noisy after reassembly, it is probably due to temporary unseating of the bearing. A light tap with a fairly heavy tool on the lamination side will shake the assembly into proper position.

The motor mounting brackets put 5⅞ inches of space between mounting hole centers. Bent brackets should be straightened to the proper dimensions. The upper and lower motors are interchangeable, if the proper pulley is used. The motor pulley may be removed from the shaft by taking out the center screw. The metal three-groove pulley is for the upper motor, the single-groove pulley for the lower.

To replace the upper belt: remove the upper compartment cover, pre-stretch the new belt, place it over one horn and then over the other, and finally place it on the desired motor pulley groove and idler pulley.

The three-groove motor pulley provides for three tremulant speeds. The center groove provides standard tremolo, the upper groove slow tremolo, and the lower groove fast tremolo.

A frayed or worn lower belt may cause noise by striking the lower shelf or belt guard. To replace this belt, remove as follows: the large center back and lower compartment cover, the eight mounting screws along the rim of the bass speaker, the connecting cable plug from the dividing network, and lift the bass speaker from the cabinet. To avoid possible cone damage, lift straight up from the shelf for a short distance.

Pull the exposed rotor support from the shaft. Place the new belt on the large pulley and pass it between the rotor and shelf towards the driving motor. To partially drop the motor remove the motor-holding wing nut nearest the cabinet back. Temporarily hook the new belt over the wing-nut screw.

Replace the bearing support on the rotor shaft and position the ends in the shallow shelf indentations adjacent to the speaker opening. Align the holes in the support with the speaker mounting holes in the shelf.

Place the bass speaker back in position and start in the two screws that hold it at each end of the bearing support. Start in the other six screws, and finally tighten all eight. Place the new belt on the driving-motor pulley and put the motor back in position with the original holding wing nut. Now adjust the belt tension by loosening the front motor wing nut and pulling the motor assembly to the left until the belt is taut. Release the assembly and the belt will assume its proper tension. Tighten the wing nut at this motor position. Do *not* attempt to stretch the belt tight or hold it in that position with the wing nut. Noise and hard starting will result.

A spring-mounted idler pulley provides proper belt tension; if the spring mounting becomes bent, it should be straightened until it is aligned with the belt.

To remove the treble speaker and/or the upper tremulant rotor:

1. Remove upper cover and belt.
2. Remove center compartment back.
3. Remove treble speaker unit plug from dividing network.
4. Remove the three screws in the treble speaker unit rim and drop straight down and out. The upper tremulant rotor may be removed by turning it sideways.

Important: When replacing these parts, be sure the rubber and metal thrust washers are on the spindle so the tremulant rotor will operate at the correct height and bass tones will not produce thrust-bearing noises. The rubber washer is placed on the spindle first, then the metal washer.

On a damaged horn reflector, cut the standoff pins so they may be pulled out with a pair of pliers.

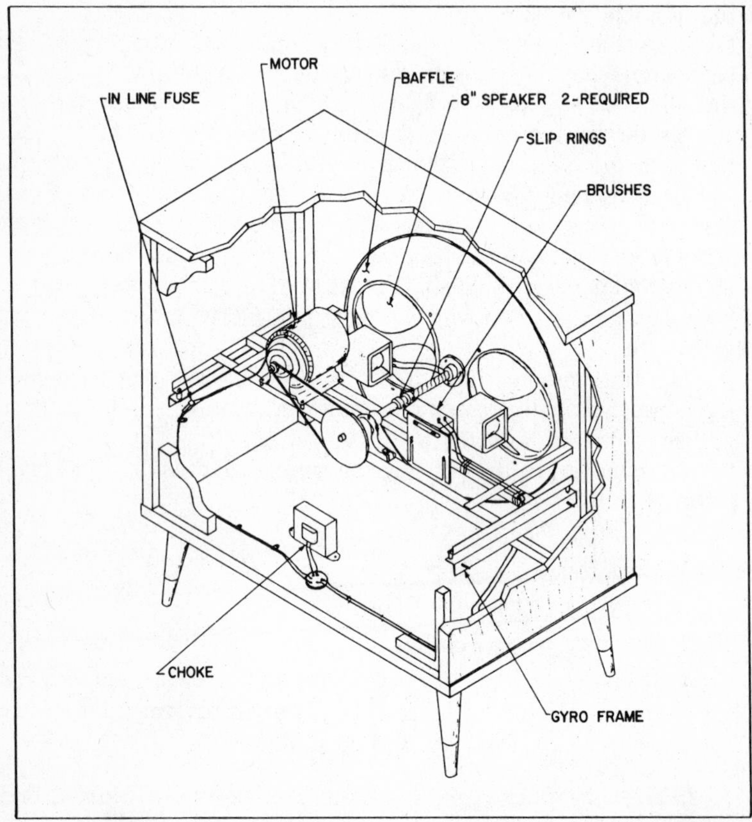

Courtesy Allen Organ Company.

Fig. 11-4. Allen Gyro Cabinet.

In assembling the new reflector, make certain the cut edge is at the top of the horn when in operating position. To hold the reflector without rattling, use the special cement furnished by the Electro Music Company.

To remove the bass speaker for replacement, remove the center compartment back and the screws in the bass speaker rim. Disconnect the plug from the dividing network. To avoid cone damage, lift the speaker straight up for a short distance before extracting it from the cabinet.

Courtesy Allen Organ Company.

Fig. 11-5. Allen Model T-44 organ.

ALLEN SPEAKER UNIT

The Allen Organ Company offers an accessory speaker unit, the external Gyro Cabinet (Fig. 11-4), for use with their Model T-44 organ (Fig. 11-5). It uses two 8-inch speakers mounted directly across from each other on a revolving assembly. Rotating the speakers has the same effect, when listening to this unit, as an amplitude modulation of the audio signal fed to the speakers.

The speakers are forced to revolve by a belt drive from the drive motor to the pulley mounted on the speaker driveshaft.

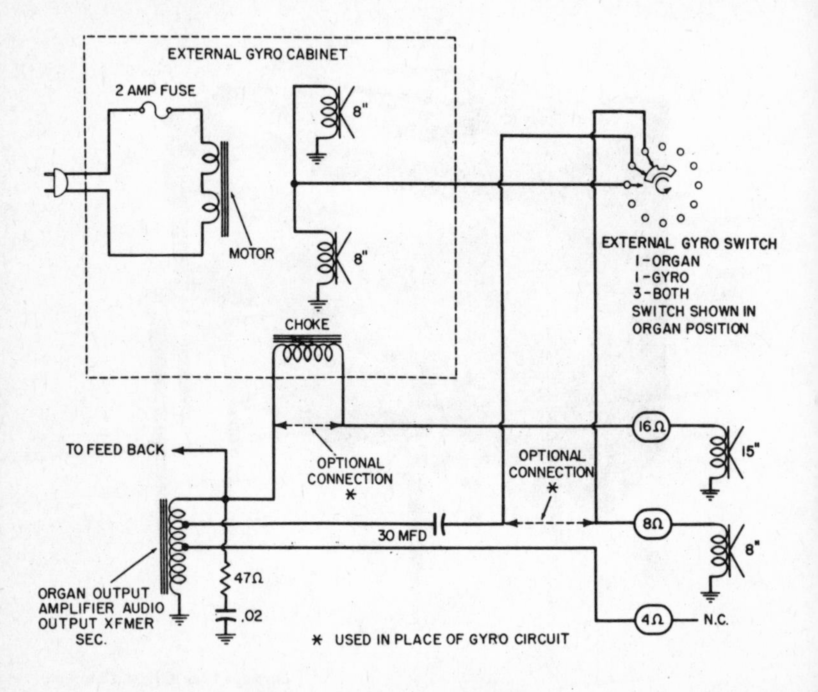

Fig. 11-6. Allen Gyro Cabinet circuit.

The speakers are mounted on this unit in such a manner as to maintain a balance of weight—important because of the mechanical rotation effects. Rotation of the speaker produces both tremolo and reverberation effects in the speaker units.

Electrical connection is made to the voice coils of the two speakers by slip rings and brushes, located at one end of the speaker driveshaft. This arrangement insures electrical contact to the speaker voice coils at all times during speaker assembly rotation. Fig. 11-6 shows the electrical schematic of this unit when connected to the main organ console.

Replacements for either speaker must be carefully selected. They should come, if possible, from the Allen Organ Company. When choosing a replacement, electrical and physical characteristics must be carefully considered. Size and weight are also important, since the speakers revolve at a fairly high rate. If a balance were not maintained, damaging vibration could occur.

GLOSSARY

Accompaniment Manual—The lower keyboard used to accompany the melody. Sometimes referred to as the lower or great manual.

Amplitude—The peak value attained by an alternating current during one complete cycle.

Attack—The period of time necessary for the tone to acquire its full intensity after the key has been depressed.

Autotransformer—A transformer in which a single tapped coil serves as both the primary and secondary.

Baffle—A partition or enclosure used with a speaker to increase the length of the air path from the front to the rear of the speaker diaphragm.

Beat Frequency—The signal produced by the interaction between two frequencies of different values.

Bourdon—A low tone of long duration.

Busbar—An electrical conductor used to make a common connection between several circuits.

Bridge-T Amplifier—An amplifier bridged between input and output to incorporate an impedance match to the preceding or succeeding stage. The bridging from input to output of a single bridge-T stage may be either resistive or capacitive.

Cent—Interval between two tones equivalent to approximately 1/100 of a semitone.

Chord—A combination of several tones sounded simultaneously.

Chromatic Scale—A scale composed entirely of half-steps.

Cipher—A tone produced on the organ when no key is being depressed.

Clavier—Any keyboard or pedalboard operated with either the hands or the feet.

Complex Tone—A sound composed of the fundamental and a number of related harmonic frequencies.

Console—The cabinet which houses the organ.

Constant-K Network—A network composed of resistance and/or capacitance-inductance in which the product of its series and shunt impedances is independent of frequency within a specific range.

Coupler—The name given a tab that allows the tones of one manual to be played with the keys of the other, or the sounding of octavely related tones on the same manual at the same time.

Coupler Rod—A rod used for intramanually connecting tone generators to a common output point.

Crossover Network—The frequency-selective circuit that divides the high and low tones for application to their respective speakers.

Decay—The fading away (diminishing in volume) of a tone after the actuated key is released. This effect may be adjusted by a switch or potentiometer on many organs to regulate the time required for the total disappearance of the tone.

Decibel—A unit of measurement (abbreviated db) used to express a change in the magnitude of the signal or sound level.

Delay Line—A transmission line so designed to delay a signal or electrical impulse for a predetermined length of time.

Diapson—Fundamental tone color of all organ music; not to be confused with any orchestral instrument, but a unique sound in itself.

Divider—A circuit so constructed that when a signal is injected at the input, the output signal will be divided by some multiple of the injected input signal frequency.

Drawbar—A device used in some electronic organs to combine various amounts of signal from the tone generators so as to simulate various instruments.

Eccles-Jordan—A type of relaxation oscillator that is triggered into conduction by a voltage pulse.

Expression Control—A control used to regulate the volume of the organ output, usually a foot pedal operated with the right foot.

Extended Octave—Tones above or below the notes on the standard keyboard which can be sounded only when specific couplers are employed.

Fast Decay—The rapid attenuation of the organ's output after release of the keyswitch.

Filter Network—A selective network of resistors, inductors, and/or capacitors which offers little opposition to certain frequencies while blocking or attenuating others.

Flat—A note moved down a half-step or semitone from its related natural pitch.

Formant Filters—A waveshaping network used to modify the signal from the tone generator so it will assume the waveshape of the desired tone.

Free Running Oscillator—An oscillator which is operating in a normal state (and at its natural frequency) until a synchronizing signal is injected to upset this condition.

Frequency—The number of complete cycles or vibrations per unit of time, usually per second.

Frequency Response—A measure of the effectiveness of a circuit or device in responding to a range of frequencies.

Fundamental Tone or Frequency—The normal pitch of a musical tone. The lowest frequency component of a complex waveform.

Gate Circuit—A circuit that operates as a selective switch and allows conduction only during selected intervals.

Great Manual—The keyboard used for playing the accompaniment to the melody. Also called the accompaniment manual or the lower manual.

Harmonic—That component of a complex note the frequency of which is a multiple of the fundamental frequency. Also called an overtone.

Interval—The difference in pitch between two tones.

Keybed—The shelf or horizontal surface on which the keyboard is mounted.

Keyswitch—The switch which is closed when a key is depressed to allow a tone from the tone generator to sound.

Keynote—The tonic, or first, note of every scale.

Manual—A group of keys played with the hands. In two-manual organs, the upper manual—referred to as the upper, solo, or swell—normally used to play the melody. The lower manual—referred to as the accompaniment, lower, or great—is usually used to play the accompaniment to the melody. In some cases, however, the melody may be played on the lower manual and the accompaniment on the upper.

Master Oscillator—An electronic circuit in the divider system that produces the highest generated frequency of each note on the scale. It also provides pulses to trigger the first divider in the tone-generator assembly.

Mechanical Tone Generator—A mechanical device used to generate the electrical impulses that are converted into audible tones.

Modulation—The process of varing the frequency, amplitude, or phase of a carrier wave.

Multivibrator—A type of relaxation oscillator usually comprising two vacuum-tube or transistor circuits connected together in such a manner that the output from the second unit is R-C coupled to the input of the first in order to set up oscillations within the circuit.

Neon Lamp—A gas-filled tube which, when ionized by application of an external voltage, will allow current to flow. Below the ionization voltage, current will not flow. Thus, it acts as an electronic switch, conducting only when sufficient voltage is applied.

Octave—The interval between two frequencies which has a ratio of 2:1.

Overtone—See Harmonic

Partial—A simple sound which contributes to the character of a complex sound or complex tone.

Pedal Divider—The divider circuit which produces the notes actuated by the foot pedals.

Pedal Generator—A tone generator used to produce the bass notes on the organ.

Pedalboard—A foot-operated keyboard (also termed Pedal Clavier) which supplies the bass accompaniment for the other manuals. It usually consists of one or two octaves.

Phase-Shift Oscillator—An oscillator in which a network having a phase shift of 180° at the oscillator frequency is connected between the output and input.

Pipe Organ—An organ in which air is forced through pipes of different lengths to produce the audible tones.

Pitch—Acuteness or gravity of a tone in relation to others or in the absolute measurement of the number and rate of its vibrations.

Potentiometer—A resistance unit having a rotating contact arm which can be set at any desired point on the resistance element.

Preset—A control which may be used to turn on or off a group of voices without the necessity of changing other tabs. They may be contained on either manual.

Regulator Tube—A type of tube used to regulate the voltage output from a power supply.

Resultant—The effect produced by two or more tones sounding together.

Reverberation—The persistence of sound due to repeated reflections.

Saturable Reactor—A magnetic core reactor, the reactance of which is controlled by changing the saturation of the core.

Scale—A series of eight consecutive whole notes.

Semitone—See Half-tone.

Sharp—A note moved up in pitch a semitone or half step.

Solo Manual—The upper manual of a two-manual organ, normally used for playing the melody. Also called Swell Manual.

Stops—The controls on the pipe organ which regulate the air passage through the various pipes.

Sustain—The effect produced by a note gradually diminishing at a regulated rate after the key has been released.

Subharmonic—An integral submultiple of the fundamental frequency of the sound to which it is related.

Swell—The upper manual of the organ. Sometimes referred to as the Solo manual.

Tablet—A type of control used to select voices and footages.

Temperament—The tuning of an instrument so the tones will be at specified intervals.

Tempered Scale—Musical pitches arranged with equal interval.

Timbre—The character or "tone color" of a musical tone. The timbre quality is determined by the intensity of the various harmonics and the frequencies of the most prominent harmonics.

Tone—The fundamental sound of any musical note.

Tone Generator—The portion of the organ generating the electrical impulses which are later modified and amplified and then converted into sound by the speaker.

Tone Wheel—A rotated disc-shape device used in mechanical tone generating systems.

Transistor—A small semiconducting device which can be used as an oscillator or amplifier.

Tremolo—An amplitude modulation of the organ tone at a rate of approximately 6.8 cps.

Tuning Fork—A U-shaped device constructed in such a way as to resonate at a predetermined frequency.

Varistor—A semiconductor device with a voltage-dependent, nonlinear resistance that drops sharply as the applied voltage is increased.

Vibrato—A frequency modulation of the organ tone at a rate of approximately 6.8 cps.

Voices—The resultant tone output which is obtained by mixing various harmonics to imitate a musical instrument or other effect.

Voicing Tab—A conrolling device for switching in filter networks between the tone generators and the audio amplifier.

Voicing Panel—The front portion of the organ which houses the voicing tabs.

Voltage Regulator—A device or circuit which maintains the output voltage at a predetermined value.

Volume—The intensity or loudness of the sound produced. Also called Expression in organ terminology.

Index

A

Accompaniment manual, 235
Allen
  pedal generators and sustain, 73-76
  percussion, 153-155
  speaker unit, 232-233
  sustain, 174-175
  tone generators, 38-40
  vibrato and tremolo, 101-103
  voicing, 183-186
Amplifier and electrical maintenance, Leslie, 222-226
Amplifiers and power supplies, 195-206
  Conn, 202
  Kinsman, 202-203
  Magnavox, 195-201
Amplitude, 235
Attack, 235
Autotransformer, 235

B

Baffle, 235
Baldwin
  keyswitches, 123-124
  percussion, 144-153
  tone generators, 24-26
  vibrato and tremolo, 87-90
Basic organ circuits, 10-20
Beat frequency, 235
Beating, 8
Bourdon, 235
Bridge-T amplifier, 235
Busbar, 235

C

Cent, 235
Chart, trouble, 210-212
Checkout procedure, 208-214
Chord, 235
Chromatic scale, 235
Cipher, 235
Circuit
  Eccles-Jordan, 15
  gate, 237
  switch, drawbar, 182
Circuits
  multivibrator, 13
  organ, basic, 10-20
  pedal voicing, 193
  voicing, 17-20
Clavier, 10, 235
Colpitts oscillator, 12

Complex tone, 235
Conn
  generator regulator, 202
  keyswitches, 114-117
  pedal generators and sustain, 49-53
  sustain, 167-170
  tone generators, 26-27
  vibrato and tremelo, 84-87
Constant-K network, 236
Console, 235
Control, expression, 236
Controls, expression, 203-206
Coupler rod, 236
Crossover network, 236

D

Decay, 236
Decibel, 236
Delay line, 236
Devices, tuning, electronic, 219-220
Diapason, 10, 236
Divider, 236
Dividing network and speaker system, Leslie, 226-227
Drawbar, 236
  switch circuit, 182

E

Eccles-Jordan circuit, 15, 236
Electron-coupled multivibrator, 16
Electronic tone generators, 23-43
  Allen, 38-40
  Baldwin, 24-26
  Conn, 26-27
  Kinsman, 40-43
  Lowrey, 31-32
  Magnavox, 35-38
  Thomas, 27-31
  Wurlitzer, 32-35
Electronic tuning devices, 219-220
Expression controls, 203-206, 236
Extended octave, 236

F

Fast decay, 236
Filter network, 236
Filters, formant, 237
Flat, 236,
Fork, tuning, 239
Formant filters, 237
Free running oscillator, 237
Frequency, 237
  beat, 235
  response, 237
Fundamental tone or frequency, 237

G

Gate circuit, 237
Generator
  pedal, 238
  regulator, Conn, 202
  tone, 239
Generators, tone
  electronic, 23-43
    Allen, 38-40

Baldwin, 24-26
Conn, 26-27
Kinsman, 40-43
Lowrey, 31-32
Magnavox, 35-38
Thomas, 27-31
Wurlitzer, 32-35
mechanical, 23-43
Great manual, 10, 237

H

Hammond
keyswitches, 111-114
pedal generators and sustain, 69-72
percussion, 129-138
vibrator and tremolo, 93-101
voicing, 182-183
Harmonic, 237
Hartley oscillator, 11

I

Interval, 237

K

Keybed, 237
Keyboard switches, lower, Thomas, 127
Keynote, 237
Keyswitches, 111-127, 237
Baldwin, 123-124
Conn, 114-117
Hammond, 111-114
Magnavox, 121-123
Thomas, 124-127
lower keyboard switches, 127
solo manual contact adjustment, 124-127
Wurlitzer, 117-121
Kinsman
amplifier and power supplies, 202-203
pedal generators and sustain, 76
percussion, 138-139
sustain, 163-167
tone generators, 40-43
vibrato and tremolo, 103-109
voicing, 186-189

L

Lamp, neon, 238
Leslie speaker units, 221-231
amplifier and electrical maintenance, 222-226
mechanical maintenance, 227-231
speaker system and dividing network, 226-227
Lower keyboard switches, Thomas, 127
Lowrey
pedal generators and sustain, 53-59
sustain, 160-163
tone generators, 31-32
vibrato and tremolo, 81-84
voicing, 191-193

M

Magnavox
- amplifiers and power supplies, 195-201
- keyswitches, 121-123
- pedal generators and sustain, 64-65
- sustain, 170-174
- tone generators, 35-38
- vibrato and tremolo, 90-92

Maintenance
- amplifier and electrical, Leslie, 222-226
- mechanical, Leslie, 227-231

Manual, 10, 237
- accompaniment, 235
- great, 237
- solo, 239

Master oscillator, 237
Mechanical
- maintenance, Leslie, 227-231
- tone generators, 22-23, 237

Modulation, 237
Multivibrator circuits, 13, 237
- electron-coupled, 16

Musical terms, 8-10

N

Neon lamp, 238
Network
- constant-K, 236
- filter, 236
- waveshaping, 18, 178

O

Octave, 238
- extended, 236

Organ
- checkout procedure, 208-214
- circuits, basic, 10-20

Oscillator
- Colpitts, 12
- free running, 237
- Hartley, 11
- master, 237
- phase-shift, 16, 78-79 238

Outphase voices, 193-194
Overtone, 238

P

Panel, voicing 240
Panoramic tone, 150-153
Partial, 238
Pedalboard, 40, 238
Pedal
- divider, 238
- generators and pedal sustain, 49-76
  - Allen, 73-76
  - Conn, 49-53
  - Hammond, 69-72
  - Kinsman, 76
  - Lowrey, 53-59
  - Magnavox, 64-65
  - Thomas, 66-68
  - Wurlitzer, 59-64
- voicing circuits, 193

Percussion, 129-155
- Allen, 153-155
- Baldwin, 144-153
- Hammond, 129-138

Kinsman, 138-139
Thomas, 139-143
Phase-shift oscillator, 16, 78-79, 238
Pipe organ, 238
Pitch, 8, 238
Potentiometer, 238
Power supplies and amplifiers, 195-206
Conn, 202
Kinsman, 202-203
Magnavox, 195-201
Preliminary tuning, 214-216
Preset, 238
Procedure
checkout, 208-214
tuning, 216-217

R

Reactor, saturable, 238
Regulator
generator, Conn, 202
tube, 238
voltage, 240
Response, frequency, 237
Resultant, 238
Reverberation, 238

S

Saturable reactor, 238
Scale, 238
chromatic, 235
tempered, 239
Semitone, 238
Sharp, 238
Solo, 10
manual, 239
contact adjustment, Thomas, 124-127
Speaker units
Allen, 232-233
Leslie, 221-231
amplifier and electrical maintenance, 222-226
mechanical maintenance, 227-231
speaker system and dividing network, 226-227
Stops, 9, 239
Subharmonic, 239
Sustain, 10, 157-175, 239
Allen, 174-175
Conn, 167-170
Kinsman, 163-167
Lowrey, 160-163
Magnavox, 170-174
Wurlitzer, 158-160
Swell, 10, 239
Switch circuit, drawbar, 182

T

Tab, voicing, 239
Tablet, 9, 239
Temperament, 239
Tempered scale, 239
Terms, musical, 8-10
Thomas
keyswitches, 124-127
lower keyboard switches, 127

solo manual contact adjustment, 124-127
pedal generators and sustain, 66-68
percussion, 139-143
tone generators, 27-31
vibrato and tremolo, 79-81
voicing, 189-191

Timbre, 8, 239

Tone, 239
complex, 235
generators, 22-23, 23-43, 237
Allen, 38-40
Baldwin, 24-26
Conn, 26-27
Kinsman, 40-43
Lowrey, 31-32
Magnavox, 35-38
Thomas, 27-31
Wurlitzer, 32-35
panoramic, 150-153
wheel, 239

Transistor, 239

Tremolo, 9, 239

Tremolo and vibrato, 77-109
Allen, 101-103
Baldwin, 87-90
Conn, 84-87
Hammond, 93-101
Kinsman, 103-109
Lowrey, 81-84
Magnavox, 90-92
Thomas, 79-81
Wurlitzer, 79

Trouble chart, 210-212

Tuning, 214-220
electronic devices, 219-220
fork method, 217-218, 239
preliminary, 214-216
procedure, 216-217

U

Unit, speaker, Allen, 232-233

V

Varistor, 239

Vibrato, 9, 239

Vibrato and tremolo, 77-109
Allen, 101-103
Baldwin, 87-90
Conn, 84-87
Hammond, 93-101
Kinsman, 103-109
Lowrey, 81-84
Magnavox, 90-92
Thomas, 79-81
Wurlitzer, 79

Voices, 10, 239
outphase, 193-194

Voicing, 17-20, 177-194
Allen, 183-186
Hammond, 182-183
Kinsman, 186-189
Lowrey, 191-193
panel, 240
tab, 239
Thomas, 189-191
Wurlitzer, 180-182

Pumps, Hydraulics, Air Compressors (AUD-40)

A comprehensive guide for engineers, operators, mechanics, students. Question and answer form. Practical information covering; power & air pumps—condensers—calculations—cooling ponds and towers—water supply—hydraulic rams—dredges—hydraulic drives—machine-tool power—accumulators—elevators—airplane control—presses—turbines—compressor classification—inter and after coolers—regulating devices—installation—lubrication—operation—maintenance—pneumatic hand tools. **$6.95**

House Heating Guide (AUD-41)

For heating, ventilating and air-conditioning engineers, plumbers, maintenance men, contractors, building superintendents and mechanics seeking practical, authentic information on heating, ventilating, air conditioning. This comprehensive reference book gives answers to 1001 questions. **$5.95**

Millwrights & Mechanics Guide (AUD-42)

Practical information on plant installation, operation, and maintenance. For millwrights, mechanics, erecting maintenance men, riggers, shopmen, servicemen, foremen, inspectors, superintendents. **$6.95**

Do-It-Yourself Encyclopedia—2 Vols. (AUD-43)

An all-in-one home repair and project guide for all do-it-yourselfers. Packed with step-by-step plans, thousands of photos, helpful charts. A really authentic, truly monumental, home-repair and home-project guide. **$8.95**

New Mechanical Dictionary (AUD-44)

The authoritative word book for mechanics, technicians and students. This dictionary gives you the new words as well as the old. Every mechanic will find his job easier if he knows the exact meaning and use of technical words that come up every day. It is an engineer's shop companion and a student's guide. **$6.95**

Water Supply & Sewage Disposal Guide (AUD-46)

Fully illustrated with detailed data on every phase of rural water-supply, septic-tank, and sewage systems. A MUST BOOK for plumbers, well drillers, home owners and farmers located outside of municipal water and sanitary service areas. **$4**

Guide to Creative Photography (AUD-47)

An informative volume for all interested in photography. Practical from first page to the last, written in simple, concise, easy-to-understand language. All technical terms are clearly defined and profusely illustrated. **$3.95**

Gas Engine Manual (AUD-48)

A completely practical book covering the construction, operation and repair of all types of modern gas engines. Part I covers gas-engine principles; engine parts; auxiliaries; timing methods; ignition systems. Part II covers troubleshooting, adjustment and repairs. **$4**

Outboard Motor & Boating Guide (AUD-49)

An essential tool for every outboard boating operator. Provides all the information needed to maintain, adjust and repair all types of outboard motors. Gives exploded views of the various parts assemblies, with relative position of each component. **$4**

Encyclopedia of Space Science—4 Vols. (AUD-50)

The whole marvelous world of space and electronics from A to Z. Four large volumes explain and clarify space and space travel. Completely up-to-date, timely coverage, including thousands of illustrations, many in full color. **$19.95**

Domestic Compact Auto Repair Manual (AUD-52)

A practical guide covering all phases of service, maintenance and repair of all popular late-model U.S. compact cars. Includes detailed step-by-step instructions on engine tune-up, fuel and carburetor systems, automatic transmissions, power steering and brakes, and electrical systems. Truly a handy reference manual for mechanics, owners, and service-men. **$5.95**

Foreign Auto Repair Manual (AUD-53)

Perfect companion to the Domestic Compact Auto Repair Manual. Contains complete, up-to-date service and repair data for the most popular imported makes, including Fiat, Hillman Minx, M.G., Opel, Peugot, Renault, SAAB, Simca, Volkswagen, and Volvo. Introductory chapters provide complete data on operation and maintenance of fuel and ignition systems. **$5**

Programmed Basic Electricity Course (AUD-54)

Completely encompasses all facets of electricity fundamentals, including basic series circuits, Ohm's law, parallel circuits, voltage, current, resistance, etc. A unique self-testing study guide for everyone interested in easily learning about electricity and electronics. 10 lessons, 1000 program frames. Perfect for self-study. **$4**

Home Workshop & Tool Handy Book (AUD-55)

The most modern, up-to-date manual ever designed for home craftsmen and do-it-yourselfers. Tells how to set up your own home workshop (basement, garage, or spare room), all about the various hand and power tools (when, where, and how to use them, etc.). Covers both wood- and metal-working principles and practices. An all-in-one workshop guide for handymen, professionals and students. **$5**

Home Modernizing & Repair Guide (AUD-56)

FOR THE "DO-IT-YOURSELFER" WHO LIKES TO DO MOST OF HIS HOME UPKEEP JOBS HIMSELF. Here is a practical guide that presents step-by-step instructions, photos, drawings, and other details for many typical home handy-man jobs. Explains what tools are needed, how to use them, and includes tips for doing a really professional job. **$2.95**

Practical Chemistry for Everyone (AUD-57)

A practical, easy-to-understand text designed for everyday reference. Comprehensive in scope, here at last is a single volume that covers the subject of chemistry on a level anyone can easily comprehend. Just the thing for those who have never studied chemistry. A useful encyclopedic volume for every home library. **$5.95**

Home Gas Heating and Appliance Manual (AUD-59)

A reliable guide to acquaint repairmen and home owners with the construction, operation, and servicing of modern gas-fired appliances such as may be found in the average home. **$3.50**

Practical Guide to Mechanics (AUD-61)

A convenient reference book valuable for its practical and concise explanations of the applicable laws of physics. Presents all the basics of mechanics in everyday language, illustrated with practical examples of their applications in various fields. **$4**

Architects & Builders Guide (AUD-69)

A valuable reference for the architect, builder, and home owner. Explains the effects of natural phenomena such as wind, fire, sound, water, and lightning on all types of buildings. Tells how to minimize their destructive effects and take advantage of their beneficial effects. **$4**

Voltage regulator, 240
Volume, 240

W

Waveshaping networks, 18, 178
Wheel, tone, 239
Wurlitzer
keyswitches, 117-121
pedal generators and sustain, 59-64
sustain, 158-160
tone generators, 32-35
vibrato and tremolo, 79
voicing, 180-182

Wiring Diagrams for Light & Power (AUD-13)

Brand-new updated edition. Electricians, wiremen, linemen, plant superintendents, construction engineers, electrical contractors and students will find these diagrams a valuable source of practical help. Each diagram is complete and self-explaining. A PRACTICAL HANDY BOOK OF ELECTRICAL HOOK-UPS. **$4**

Refrigeration & Air Conditioning Guide (AUD-14)

4 BOOKS IN ONE, covering basic principles, servicing, operation, repair. Covers household refrigeration, special refrigeration units, commercial and industrial refrigeration, and air-conditioning systems. A gold mine of essential important facts for engineers, servicemen and users. **$6**

New Electric Library—10 Vols. (AUD-15A)

For engineers, electricians, electrical workers, mechanics and students. Presenting in simple, concise form the fundamental principles, rules and applications of applied electricity. Fully illustrated with diagrams and sketches, also calculations and tables for ready reference. Based on the best knowledge and experience of applied electricity.

Vol. 1 (AUD-15)—Electricity, magnetism, armature winding, repairs.
Vol. 2 (AUD-16)—Dynamos, DC motors, construction, installation, maintenance, troubleshooting.
Vol. 3 (AUD-17)—Electrical testing instruments, storage battery construction and repairs.
Vol. 4 (AUD-18)—Alternating current principles and diagrams, power factor, alternators, transformers.
Vol. 5 (AUD-19)—AC motors, converters, switches, fuses, circuit breakers.
Vol. 6 (AUD-20)—Relays, capacitors, regulators, rectifiers, meters, switchboards, power-station practice.
Vol. 7 (AUD-21)—Wiring, high-tension transmission, plans, calculations.
Vol. 8 (AUD-22)—Railways, signals, elevators.
Vol. 9 (AUD-23)—Radio, telephone, telegraph, television, motion pictures.
Vol. 10 (AUD-24)—Refrigeration, illumination, welding, X-ray, modern electrical appliances.

COMPLETE SET $25.00 **$3 a volume**

Answers on Blueprint Reading (AUD-25)

Covers all types of blueprint reading for mechanics and builders. The man who can read blueprints is in line for a better job. This book gives you this secret language, step by step in easy stages. NO OTHER TRADE BOOK LIKE IT. **$3.95**

Masons & Builders Guides—4 Vols. (AUD-26)

A practical illustrated trade assistant on modern construction for bricklayers, stone masons, cement workers, plasterers, and tile setters. Explains in clear language and with detailed illustrations all the principles, advances and short cuts based on modern practice—including how to figure and calculate various jobs.

Vol. 1—Brick work, bricklaying, bonding, designs.
Vol. 2—Brick foundations, arches, tile setting, estimates.
Vol. 3—Concrete mixing, placing forms, reinforced stucco.
Vol. 4—Plastering, stone masonry, steel construction, blueprints.
$3.00 a volume. **$10.50**

Electric Motor Guide (AUD-27)

Covers the construction, hook-up, control, maintenance and troubleshooting of all types of motors including armature winding. A handy guide for electricians and all electrical workers. **$5.95**

Oil Burner Guide (AUD-28)

A practical, concise treatise explaining in detail both domestic and industrial oil burners, including electrical hook-ups and wiring diagrams. Fully covering the theory, construction, installation, operation, testing, servicing and repair of all oil-burner equipment. Fully indexed for quick reference. **$3.95**

Pumps, Hydraulics, Air Compressors (AUD-40)

A comprehensive guide for engineers, operators, mechanics, students. Question and answer form. Practical information covering; power & air pumps—condensers—calculations—cooling ponds and towers—water supply—hydraulic rams—dredges—hydraulic drives—machine-tool power—accumulators—elevators—airplane control—presses—turbines—compressor classification—inter and after coolers—regulating devices—installation—lubrication—operation—maintenance—pneumatic hand tools. **$6.95**

House Heating Guide (AUD-41)

For heating, ventilating and air-conditioning engineers, plumbers, maintenance men, contractors, building superintendents and mechanics seeking practical, authentic information on heating, ventilating, air conditioning. This comprehensive reference book gives answers to 1001 questions. **$5.95**

Millwrights & Mechanics Guide (AUD-42)

Practical information on plant installation, operation, and maintenance. For millwrights, mechanics, erecting maintenance men, riggers, shopmen, servicemen, foremen, inspectors, superintendents. **$6.95**

Do-It-Yourself Encyclopedia—2 Vols. (AUD-43)

An all-in-one home repair and project guide for all do-it-yourselfers. Packed with step-by-step plans, thousands of photos, helpful charts. A really authentic, truly monumental, home-repair and home-project guide. **$8.95**

New Mechanical Dictionary (AUD-44)

The authoritative word book for mechanics, technicians and students. This dictionary gives you the new words as well as the old. Every mechanic will find his job easier if he knows the exact meaning and use of technical words that come up every day. It is an engineer's shop companion and a student's guide. **$6.95**

Water Supply & Sewage Disposal Guide (AUD-46)

Fully illustrated with detailed data on every phase of rural water-supply, septic-tank, and sewage systems. A MUST BOOK for plumbers, well drillers, home owners and farmers located outside of municipal water and sanitary service areas. **$4**

Guide to Creative Photography (AUD-47)

An informative volume for all interested in photography. Practical from first page to the last, written in simple, concise, easy-to-understand language. All technical terms are clearly defined and profusely illustrated. **$3.95**

Gas Engine Manual (AUD-48)

A completely practical book covering the construction, operation and repair of all types of modern gas engines. Part I covers gas-engine principles; engine parts; auxiliaries; timing methods; ignition systems. Part II covers troubleshooting, adjustment and repairs. **$4**

Outboard Motor & Boating Guide (AUD-49)

An essential tool for every outboard boating operator. Provides all the information needed to maintain, adjust and repair all types of outboard motors. Gives exploded views of the various parts assemblies, with relative position of each component. **$4**

Encyclopedia of Space Science—4 Vols. (AUD-50)

The whole marvelous world of space and electronics from A to Z. Four large volumes explain and clarify space and space travel. Completely up-to-date, timely coverage, including thousands of illustrations, many in full color. **$19.95**

Domestic Compact Auto Repair Manual (AUD-52)

A practical guide covering all phases of service, maintenance and repair of all popular late-model U.S. compact cars. Includes detailed step-by-step instructions on engine tune-up, fuel and carburetor systems, automatic transmissions, power steering and brakes, and electrical systems. Truly a handy reference manual for mechanics, owners, and service-men. **$5.95**

Foreign Auto Repair Manual (AUD-53)

Perfect companion to the Domestic Compact Auto Repair Manual. Contains complete, up-to-date service and repair data for the most popular imported makes, including Fiat, Hillman Minx, M.G., Opel, Peugot, Renault, SAAB, Simca, Volkswagen, and Volvo. Introductory chapters provide complete data on operation and maintenance of fuel and ignition systems. **$5**

Programmed Basic Electricity Course (AUD-54)

Completely encompasses all facets of electricity fundamentals, including basic series circuits, Ohm's law, parallel circuits, voltage, current, resistance, etc. A unique self-testing study guide for everyone interested in easily learning about electricity and electronics. 10 lessons, 1000 program frames. Perfect for self-study. **$4**

Home Workshop & Tool Handy Book (AUD-55)

The most modern, up-to-date manual ever designed for home craftsmen and do-it-yourselfers. Tells how to set up your own home workshop (basement, garage, or spare room), all about the various hand and power tools (when, where, and how to use them, etc.). Covers both wood- and metal-working principles and practices. An all-in-one workshop guide for handymen, professionals and students. **$5**

Home Modernizing & Repair Guide (AUD-56)

FOR THE "DO-IT-YOURSELFER" WHO LIKES TO DO MOST OF HIS HOME UPKEEP JOBS HIMSELF. Here is a practical guide that presents step-by-step instructions, photos, drawings, and other details for many typical home handy-man jobs. Explains what tools are needed, how to use them, and includes tips for doing a really professional job. **$2.95**

Practical Chemistry for Everyone (AUD-57)

A practical, easy-to-understand text designed for everyday reference. Comprehensive in scope, here at last is a single volume that covers the subject of chemistry on a level anyone can easily comprehend. Just the thing for those who have never studied chemistry. A useful encyclopedic volume for every home library. **$5.95**

Home Gas Heating and Appliance Manual (AUD-59)

A reliable guide to acquaint repairmen and home owners with the construction, operation, and servicing of modern gas-fired appliances such as may be found in the average home. **$3.50**

Practical Guide to Mechanics (AUD-61)

A convenient reference book valuable for its practical and concise explanations of the applicable laws of physics. Presents all the basics of mechanics in everyday language, illustrated with practical examples of their applications in various fields. **$4**

Architects & Builders Guide (AUD-69)

A valuable reference for the architect, builder, and home owner. Explains the effects of natural phenomena such as wind, fire, sound, water, and lightning on all types of buildings. Tells how to minimize their destructive effects and take advantage of their beneficial effects. **$4**

Pittman, Carl
Audels practical guide to
servicing electronic organs

AUDEL GUIDES HELP YOU

for Mechanics, Engineers, Technicians,

Read Modern **AUDEL GUIDES** for Profit!

Every mechanic, engineer, helper, technician and hobbyist can improve his present knowledge, and earning power, by reading modern AUDEL Guides. These helpful pocket educators are practical books, containing down-to-earth, useful information on theory and practice.

AUDEL Guides are well illustrated and easy to understand. They are world-famous for saving time, worry and money . . . as hundreds of thousands of present readers can attest.

AUDEL Guides provide you with an opportunity to *learn more and earn more.* Decide for yourself which titles would be most helpful to you. If your bookstore does not have all the titles you require, we will gladly send any Guides for FREE EXAMINATION in your home—at our risk and with no obligation to you.

APPLIANCE SERVICING

Home Appliance Service Guide

AUTOMOTIVE GUIDES

Gas Engine Manual
Auto Mechanics Guide
Truck & Tractor Guide
Diesel Engine Manual
Domestic Compact Auto Repair Manual
Foreign Auto Repair Manual

BOATING

Outboard Motor & Boating Guide

BUILDING TRADES GUIDES

Water Supply & Sewage Disposal Guide
Answers on Blue Print Reading
Sheet Metal Pattern Layouts
Sheet Metal Workers Handy Book
Carpenters & Builders Guides (4 vols.)
Plumbers & Steamfitters Guides (4 vols.)
Masons & Builders Guides (4 vols.)
House Heating Guide
Millwrights & Mechanics Guide

DO-IT-YOURSELF GUIDES

Guide to Creative Photography
Do-It-Yourself Encyclopedia (2 vols.)
Home Appliance Service Guide
Home Workshop & Tool Handy Book

DRAFTING GUIDES

Answers on Blue Print Reading
Mechanical Drawing
Rogers Drawing and Design

ELECTRICITY GUIDES

Home Appliance Service Guide
Electric Motor Guide
Handy Book of Practical Electricity
Wiring Diagrams for Light & Power
New Electricity Library—10 vols.
Electrical Power Calculations
New Electric Dictionary
Questions & Answers for Electricians Examinations
Programmed Basic Electricity Course

AUDEL GUIDES... *famous since 1879 as practical, helpful self-educators*